Challenging Word Problems

Published by Marshall Cavendish Education
An imprint of Marshall Cavendish International (Singapore) Private Limited
Times Centre, 1 New Industrial Road, Singapore 536196
Customer Service Hotline: (65) 6411 0820
E-mail: tmesales@sg.marshallcavendish.com
Website: www.marshallcavendish.com/education

First published 2011

ISBN 978-981-28-5533-6

Printed in Singapore by Times Printers, www.timesprinters.com

Distributed in the U.S.A. by SingaporeMath.com Inc

SingaporeMath.com Inc

The Publisher would like to recognize the contribution of Jennifer Hoerst (Curriculum Advisor, SingaporeMath.com Inc) to Primary Mathematics Challenging Word Problems.

Preface

PRIMARY MATHEMATICS **Challenging Word Problems** provides graded exercises for students of mixed abilities and challenging questions for better math students. This series is written to supplement Singapore's **Primary Mathematics** textbooks, both U.S. and Standards editions, distributed by SingaporeMath.com, Inc. for use in the U.S.A.

Adopting a topical approach in which mathematical concepts and skills are taught and reinforced, the **Challenging Word Problems** series serves to improve students' problem-solving skills and enhance their mathematical reasoning.

Each book in the series features the following:

- **Worked Examples** for each topic show common methods of solution used in the Primary Mathematics textbooks;
- **Practice Questions** allow students to apply and practice questions similar to the ones discussed in the Worked Examples and in the Primary Mathematics textbooks;
- **Challenging Problems** provide opportunities for more capable students to solve higher-order word problems and further develop their problem-solving skills;
- **Mixed Problems** allow students to test their understanding of the concepts discussed in earlier topics and in the Primary Mathematics textbooks;
- **Answers** allow teachers or students to check their answers to all practice exercises and challenging problems;
- **Worked solutions** provide commonly used methods of solving non-routine questions, while encouraging creative or intuitive ones as well.

A student's guide to using the **Challenging Word Problems** series effectively.

1. Read each question given in the Worked Example. Try to solve it before reading the solution.

2. If your solution is similar to the one given in the Worked Example, well done. If you have used a different method, yet have arrived at the same answer, great – you now have at least two methods of solving this question.

3. If your answer is different, look at your work again and figure out where you may have gone wrong.

4. If you have understood all the worked examples, proceed to the Practice Questions; then check your answers with the ones at the back of the book. Should you get stuck at any question, don't panic; go through it again. If you still find difficulty in solving the question, seek help from your friend or teacher.

5. If you have understood and solved all the Practice Questions, you are now ready to try the Challenging Problems. Do them on your own first. Seek help only if you need some hints or clarification.

6. Try to come up with similar questions and challenge your friends to solve them. For a given question, discuss some possible solutions that you may have used in arriving at the answer.

Contents

1 Whole Numbers

Worked Example 1

Mrs. Jones has 33 coins. She gives them out to Ann, Beth, Corinne, Denise, and Ethel who are seated around a table. She gives the first coin to Ann, the second coin to Beth, and so on until all the coins are given out. Who does she give the last coin to?

Method 1

Ann	Beth	Corinne	Denise	Ethel
1	2	3	4	5
6	7	8	9	10
11	12	13	14	15
⋮	⋮	⋮	⋮	⋮
31	32	33		

She gives the last coin to **Corinne**.

Method 2

To determine who receives the last coin, look at the remainder (R) obtained when the number of coins is divided by 5 people.

If R = 0, the last coin goes to Ethel. If R = 1, the last coin goes to Ann. If R = 2, the last coin goes to Beth. If R = 3, the last coin goes to Corinne. If R = 4, the last coin goes to Denise.

$33 \div 5 = 6 \text{ R } 3$

She gives the last coin to **Corinne**.

Worked Example 2

Amos was paid a $5 bonus for each package that he delivered on time, and got $2 deducted for every late delivery. After delivering 30 packages, he was given a bonus of $101. How many packages did he deliver late?

If Amos delivered all 30 packages on time, his bonus would be $30 \times \$5 = \$150$.

For every late delivery, $\$5 + \$2 = \$7$ was deducted.

Total amount deducted = $150 – $101
= $49

Number of packages delivered late = $49 ÷ $7
= 7

He delivered **7** packages late.

Practice Questions

Answer all questions.

1. Mr. Lee gives 100 stickers to Aaron, Cathy, Esther, Ginny, Ian, and Karen who are seated in a circle. Aaron gets the first sticker, Cathy gets the second sticker, and so on until all the stickers are given out. Who gets the last sticker from Mr. Lee?

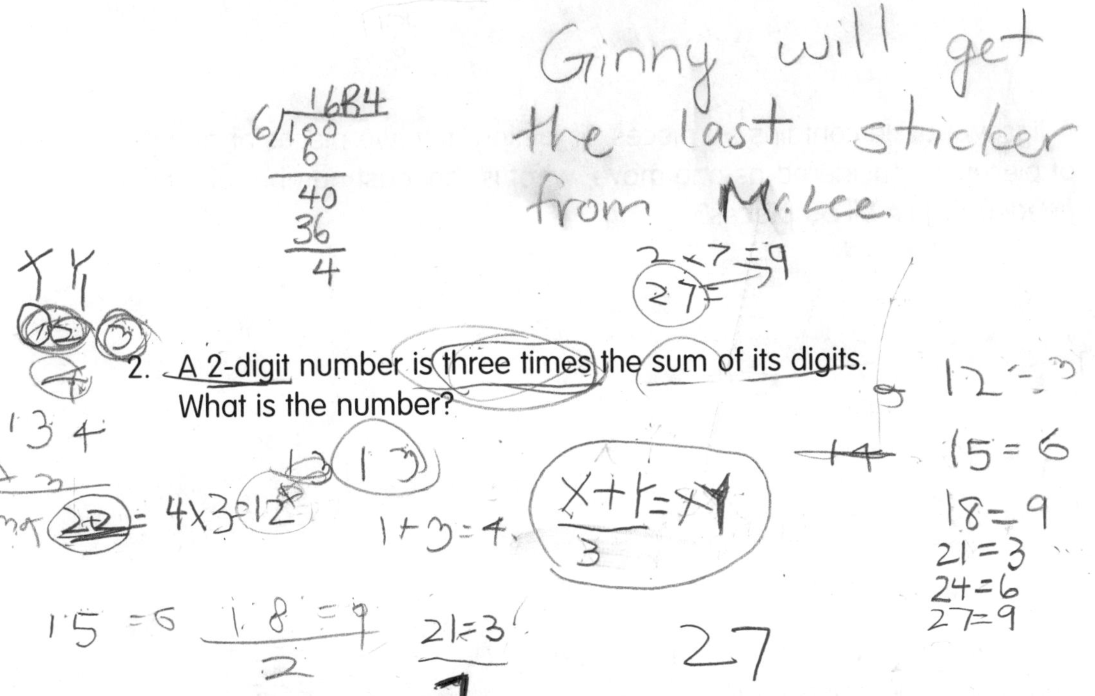

2. A 2-digit number is three times the sum of its digits. What is the number?

3. Louis wants to arrange his CD collection in stacks of equal size. After arranging in stacks of 2, stacks of 3, and then stacks of 5, he finds that there is always 1 CD left over. What is the least possible number of CDs Louis could have in his collection?

4. The pages of a textbook are numbered consecutively from 1 to 100. How many page numbers contain the digit 2 but are not divisible by 2?

5 numbers

5. A jigsaw puzzle contains 50 pieces. If joining any two pieces or groups of pieces is considered as one move, what is the least number of moves needed to join all 50 pieces?

49 moves

6. Jill threw some darts at the board on the right and scored 100 points in all.
   (a) How many darts did she throw?
   (b) Where did the darts land on the board?

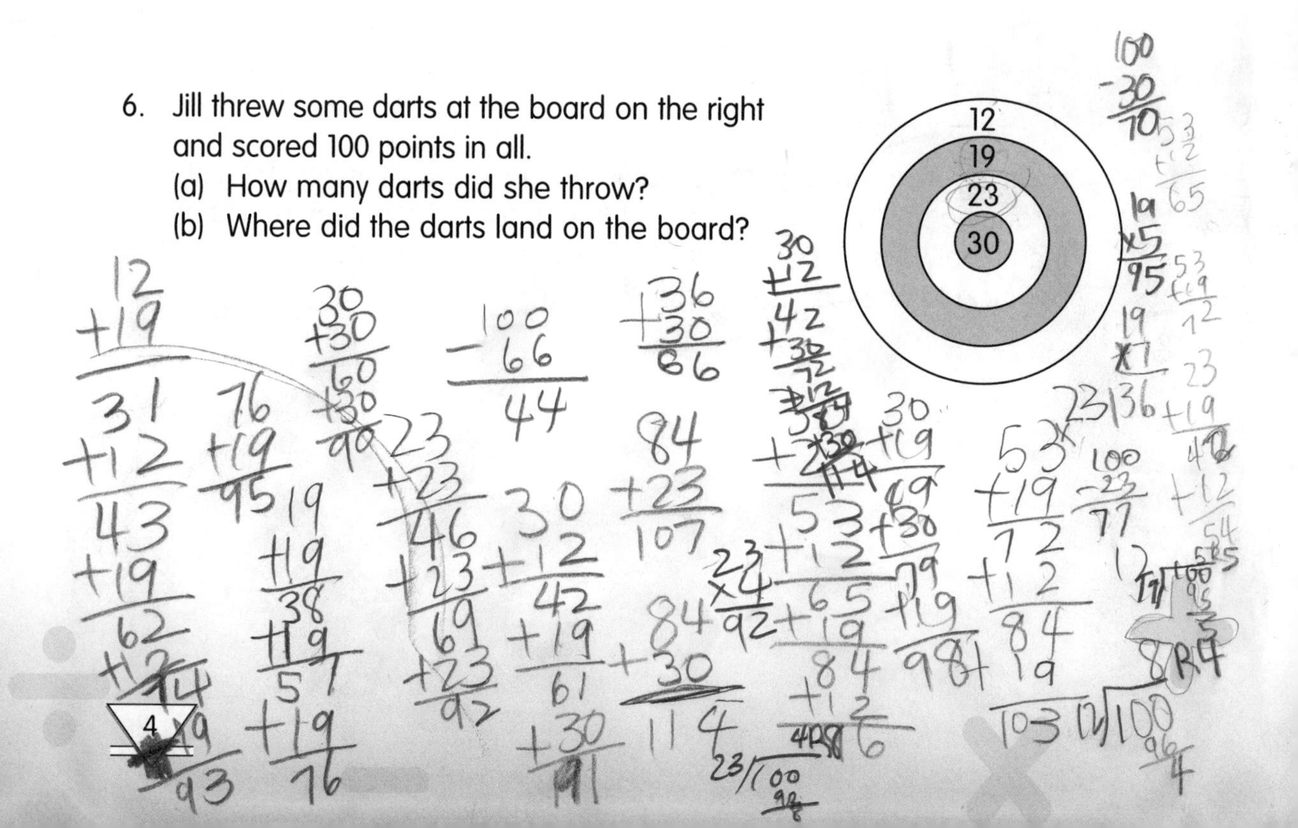

7. Six tennis players joined a tournament where each player played against each other once. How many games were played in all?

8. The sum of ten numbers is 2783. If one of the ten numbers is changed from 397 to 502, what is the new sum?

9. There were 12 toys in Bag P and 66 toys in Bag Q. After Mrs. Murray added the same number of toys into each bag, Bag Q had 3 times as many toys as Bag P. How many toys did she add into each bag?

10. Joseph had 28 magnets and Sarah had 157 magnets. After each of them added the same number of magnets to their collection, Sarah had 4 times as many magnets as Joseph. How many magnets did each of them add to their collection?

11. Olivia had 32 stamps and Sally had 154 stamps. After each of them bought the same number of stamps, Sally had three times as many stamps as Olivia. How many stamps did they buy in all?

Challenging Problems

Worked Example 1

How many 4-digit numbers can be formed using the digits 0, 1, and 2?

The first digit of the number can be either 1 or 2 — there are 2 choices.

Each of the remaining digits can be 0, 1 or 2 — there are 3 choices.

Number of 4 digit numbers formed $= 2 \times 3 \times 3 \times 3$
$= \mathbf{54}$

Worked Example 2

How many pairs of whole numbers sum up to 43? Out of these pairs, how many of them have a difference of 17?

Use a systematic list.

43 + 0	42 + 1	41 + 2	40 + 3
39 + 4	38 + 5	37 + 6	36 + 7
35 + 8	34 + 9	33 + 10	32 + 11
31 + 12	30 + 13	29 + 14	28 + 15
27 + 16	26 + 17	25 + 18	24 + 19
23 + 20	22 + 21		

22 pairs of numbers sum up to 43.

One pair of numbers (30 and 13) has a difference of 17.

Answer all questions.

1. When Number X is divided by Number Y, the quotient is 16 and the remainder is 3. The sum of the two numbers, the quotient, and the remainder is 345. What is Number X?

2. At the start of a trip, the odometer in Frank's car had a reading of 12,321, which is a palindromic number. After driving for 2 hours, the odometer showed another reading, which is also a palindromic number. If Frank was driving below a speed limit of 100 km/h, what was his speed?

A palindromic number reads the same forward and backward.

3. The product of the ages of two adults is 770. What is the sum of their ages?

4. How many 3-digit numbers have a remainder of 7 when divided by 9, and a remainder of 2 when divided by 5?

5. At an election, a total of 240 votes were cast for four candidates. The winner won by a margin of 8, 13, and 15 votes over the other three candidates. What is the lowest number of votes received by a candidate?

6. Two watches and one calculator cost $49 in all. Three watches and three calculators cost $99 in all. What is the cost of one watch?

7. Two bags and four hats cost $100 in all. Three bags and seven hats cost $164 in all. What is the cost of one hat?

8. Three watches and five lamps cost $176 in all. Five watches and three lamps cost $208 in all. What is the cost of one lamp?

9. Three calculators cost as much as seven mugs. Each calculator costs $12 more than each mug. What is the cost of one mug?

10. Three jackets cost as much as five shirts. Each jacket costs $16 more than each shirt. What is the cost of one shirt?

2 Fractions

Worked Example 1

A balanced scale has a packet of sugar on its right pan. On its left pan, it has a packet of salt and a $\frac{2}{3}$-kg weight. The packet of salt is $\frac{2}{3}$ of the weight of the packet of sugar. What is the weight of the packet of sugar?

packet of sugar

Right pan

Left pan

packet of salt

$\frac{2}{3}$-kg weight

1 unit ⟶ $\frac{2}{3}$ kg

3 units ⟶ $3 \times \frac{2}{3}$ kg = 2 kg

The weight of the packet of sugar is **2 kg**.

Worked Example 2

Richard spent $\frac{3}{4}$ of a sum of money and gave away $\frac{3}{4}$ of the remainder. He had \$6 left. How much did he have at first?

Method 1

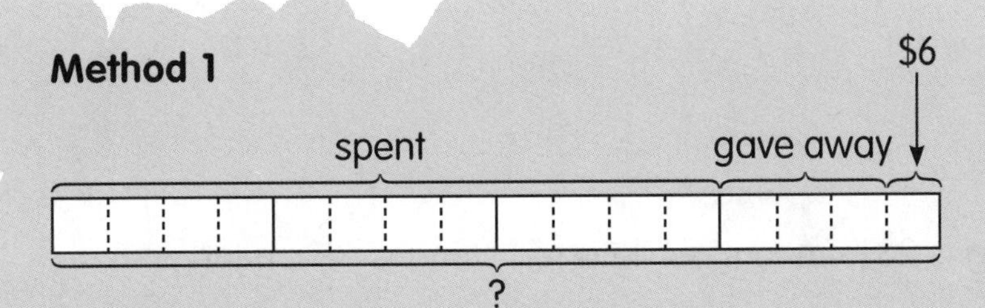

1 unit ⟶ \$6

16 units ⟶ $16 \times \$6 = \$96$

He had **\$96** at first.

Method 2

$\frac{1}{4}$ of the remainder ⟶ \$6

$\frac{4}{4}$ of the remainder ⟶ $4 \times \$6 = \$24$

Fraction left after spending $= 1 - \frac{3}{4}$

$= \frac{1}{4}$

$\frac{1}{4}$ of the sum of money ⟶ \$24

$\frac{4}{4}$ of the sum of money ⟶ $4 \times \$24 = \$96$

He had **\$96** at first.

Answer all questions.

1. Lisa mixed $\frac{1}{2}$ kg of flour, $\frac{1}{3}$ kg of butter, and $\frac{1}{4}$ kg of sugar to make batter. What is the total weight of the batter?

2. A blue string is $23\frac{1}{4}$ cm long while a red string is $9\frac{2}{5}$ cm long. How much longer is the blue string than the red string?

3. The distance of a relay race was 3 km. Zoe ran $\frac{2}{5}$ of the distance. How many kilometers did she run?

4. Tommy has a rectangular strip of paper that is 21 cm long. If he cuts it into smaller pieces, each $2\frac{1}{3}$ cm long, how many pieces of paper will he have?

5. A balanced scale has a bag of flour on its right pan. On its left pan, it has a bag of rice and a 1-kg weight. The bag of rice is half the weight of the bag of flour. What is the weight of 2 similar bags of flour?

6. Sam spent $\frac{1}{2}$ of a sum of money on a book, and $\frac{1}{2}$ of the remainder on a bag of candy. He had $2 left. How much did he pay for the book?

7. Mr. Rafik spent $\frac{1}{4}$ of a sum of money on a television set, and $\frac{2}{3}$ of the remainder on a coffee table. He saved the remaining $120. How much did he have at first?

8. Xavier spent $\frac{3}{10}$ of his money on a lawn mower, and $\frac{2}{3}$ of the remainder on a barbecue grill. If he paid $336 for the barbecue grill, how much did he pay for the lawn mower?

9. Charles spent $\frac{1}{4}$ of his allowance on a shirt, and $\frac{2}{5}$ of the remainder on a book.
   (a) What fraction of his allowance did he have left?
   (b) If he spent $18 on the book, how much did he have at first?

10. A bag contains some red, blue, yellow, and green marbles. $\frac{3}{10}$ of the marbles are red, $\frac{2}{5}$ are green, and the rest are blue or yellow. There are twice as many blue marbles as yellow marbles. There are 17 fewer blue marbles than red marbles. How many marbles are there in all?

Challenging Problems

Worked Example 1

There is a total of 276 beads in Packet A and Packet B. There are 36 fewer beads in Packet B than $\frac{4}{9}$ of the number of beads in Packet A. How many beads are there in Packet A?

Packet A
Packet B 36
4 units
276

13 units ⟶ $276 + 36 = 312$
1 unit ⟶ $312 \div 13 = 24$
9 units ⟶ $9 \times 24 = 216$

There are **216** beads in Packet A.

Worked Example 2

A ball is dropped onto the floor from a height of 128 cm. It rebounds to half of the height from where it was dropped, and this carries on for each subsequent rebound. How many centimeters has the ball covered by the time it hits the floor for the fourth time?

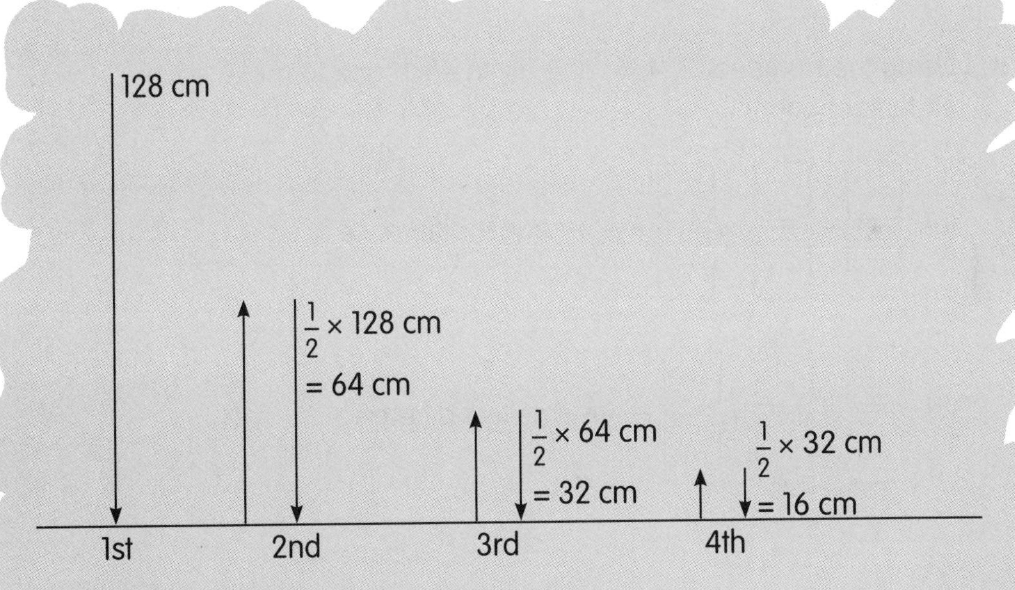

$128 \text{ cm} + 2 \times 64 \text{ cm} + 2 \times 32 \text{ cm} + 2 \times 16 \text{ cm}$
$= 128 \text{ cm} + 128 \text{ cm} + 64 \text{ cm} + 32 \text{ cm}$
$= 352 \text{ cm}$

The ball has covered **352 cm** by the time it hits the floor for the fourth time.

Answer all questions.

1. Without converting the fractions to decimals, state which of these fractions are smaller than $\frac{1}{5}$.

   A. $\frac{5}{21}$ B. $\frac{7}{36}$ C. $\frac{15}{72}$ D. $\frac{26}{101}$

2. Using the numbers 2, 4, 6, or 8, fill in each box to make each statement correct.

   (a) $\frac{\square}{\square} - \frac{\square}{\square} = \frac{\square}{\square}$ ⟶ largest difference

   (b) $\frac{\square}{\square} - \frac{\square}{\square} = \frac{\square}{\square}$ ⟶ smallest difference

3. A fraction becomes $\frac{2}{3}$ when simplified. The product of its numerator and denominator is 216. What is the fraction?

4. Shirley had 52 more coins than Jim after Jim gave $\frac{1}{5}$ of his coins to her. If they both had 260 coins in all, how many coins did Shirley have at first?

5. Ryan and Marie had some marbles. If Ryan lost 15 marbles, he would have 4 times as many marbles as Marie. If Ryan lost 75 marbles, he would have $1\frac{1}{2}$ times as many marbles as Marie. How many marbles did Ryan have at first?

6. Ruth and Bob have $130 in all. Ruth and Kevin have $115 in all. If Bob has $1\frac{1}{2}$ times as much money as Kevin, how much money does Ruth have?

7. Larry and Steve have 171 marbles in all. The number of marbles Larry has is 39 fewer than $\frac{3}{7}$ of the number of marbles Steve has. How many marbles does Steve have?

8. In Farm A, $\frac{4}{5}$ of the number of sheep are equal to $\frac{1}{2}$ of the number of sheep in Farm B. The total number of sheep in Farm A and Farm B is 845. How many sheep are there in Farm B?

9. Martha and Mary had 375 jelly beans in all. After Mary ate 24 jelly beans and Martha ate $\frac{1}{7}$ of her jelly beans, they each had the same number of jelly beans left. How many jelly beans did each girl have at first?

10. Adrian wants his lawn to be mown. Three men apply for the task. The first man can mow the lawn in 6 h; the second man can mow the lawn in 4 h; and the third man can mow the lawn in 3 h. How long will it take for the three men to complete the task?

3 Area and Perimeter

Worked Example 1

The perimeter of a rectangle is 62 cm. Its length is 18 cm. What is its area?

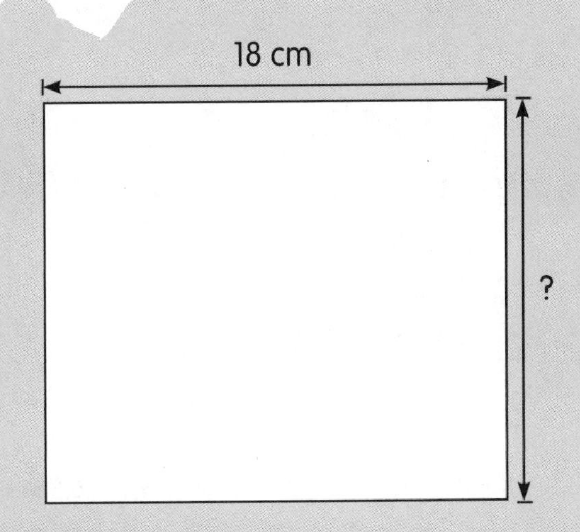

Perimeter = 2 × (length + width)
= 62 cm

Length + width = 62 cm ÷ 2
= 31 cm

Width = 31 cm − 18 cm
= 13 cm

Area = 18 cm × 13 cm
= 234 cm^2

Its area is **234 cm^2**.

Worked Example 2

Find the perimeter and area of the figure below.

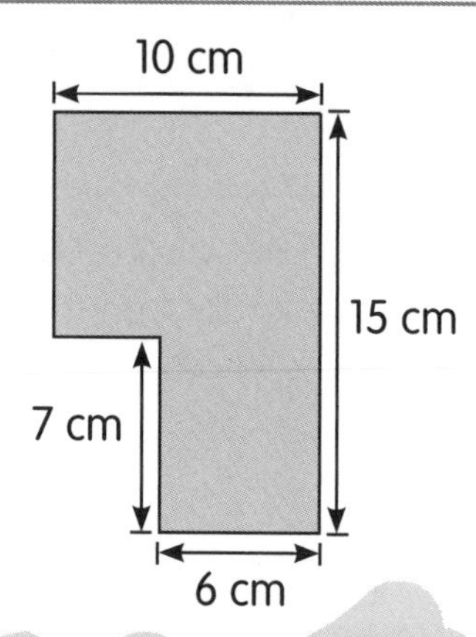

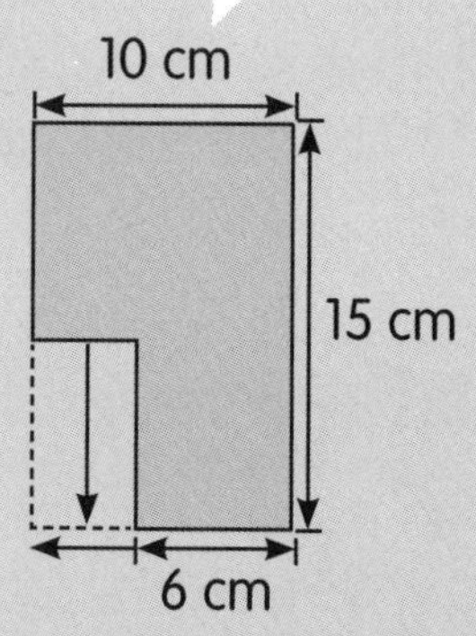

Perimeter = $2 \times (10 \text{ cm} + 15 \text{ cm})$
= 50 cm

Its perimeter is **50 cm**.

We can use the three methods below to find the area of the figure.

Method 1

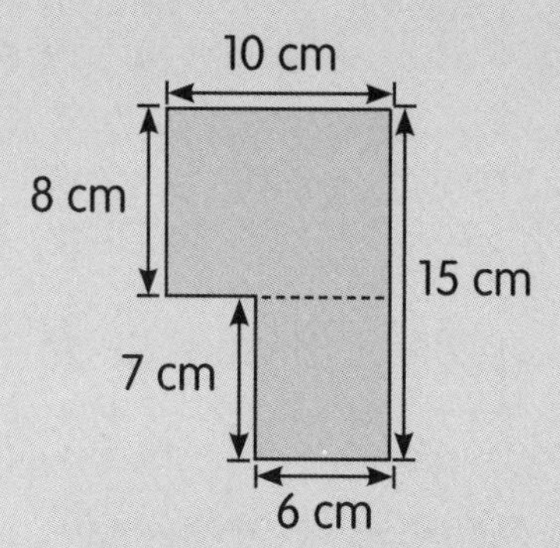

Area = $(10 \text{ cm} \times 8 \text{ cm}) + (7 \text{ cm} \times 6 \text{ cm})$
= $80 \text{ cm}^2 + 42 \text{ cm}^2$
= 122 cm^2

Method 2

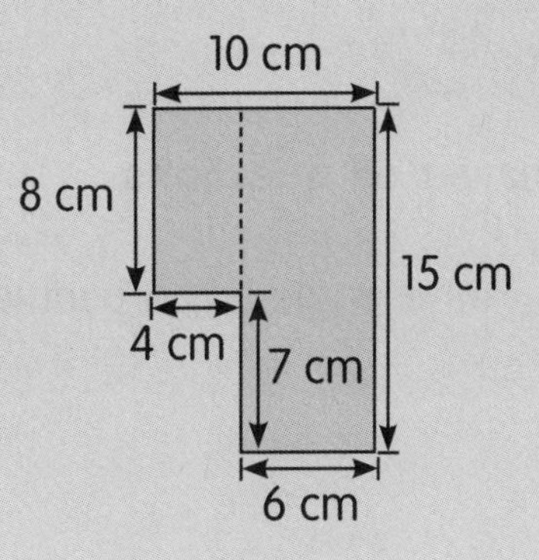

$$\text{Area} = (8 \text{ cm} \times 4 \text{ cm}) + (15 \text{ cm} \times 6 \text{ cm})$$
$$= 32 \text{ cm}^2 + 90 \text{ cm}^2$$
$$= 122 \text{ cm}^2$$

Method 3

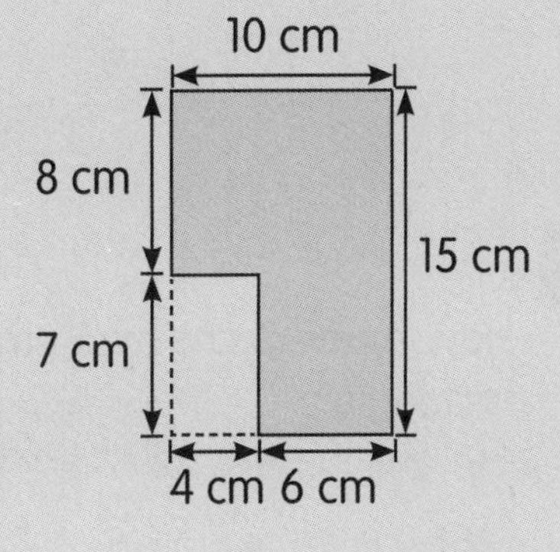

$$\text{Area} = (15 \text{ cm} \times 10 \text{ cm}) - (7 \text{ cm} \times 4 \text{ cm})$$
$$= 150 \text{ cm}^2 - 28 \text{ cm}^2$$
$$= 122 \text{ cm}^2$$

Its area is **122 cm^2**.

Answer all questions.

1. A rectangle has a perimeter of 78 cm. If its width is 17 cm, find its area.

2 How many 3 cm by 5 cm rectangles can be cut from a 6 cm by 10 cm rectangle?

3. How many 10-cm square floor tiles are needed to cover a floor that measures 6 m by 8 m?

4. The perimeter of a square floor is 32 m. What is the cost of carpeting the floor at $8 per square meter?

5. A square and a rectangle have the same area. The rectangle has a length of 16 cm and a perimeter of 50 cm. What is the length of the square?

6. The length of a rectangle is three times its width. If its perimeter is 72 cm, what is its area?

7. The figure below shows a rectangular field. It has a 5-m wide path around it. Find the area of the path.

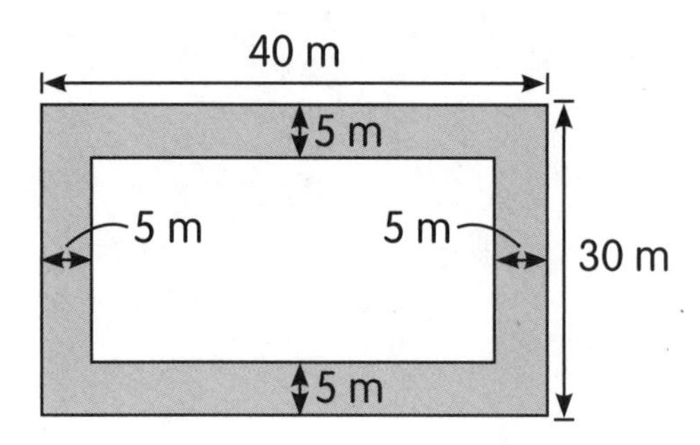

8. Find the area of the figure shown.

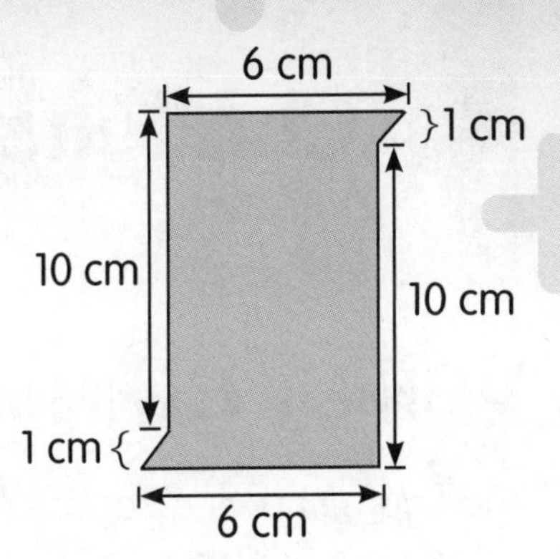

9. The figure below is made up of two identical overlapping rectangles. Each rectangle measures 25 cm by 8 cm. What is the area of the figure?

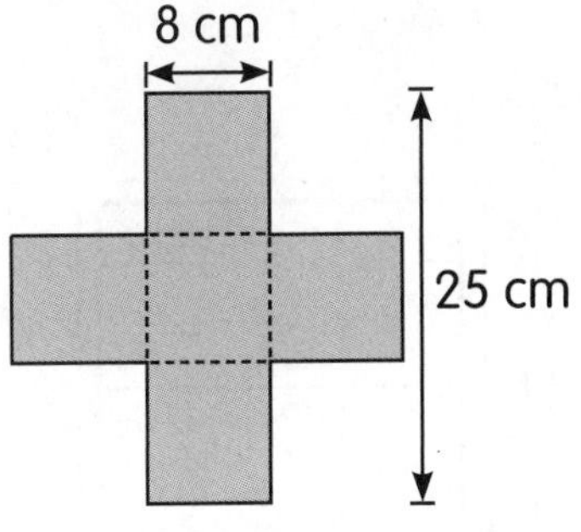

10. Gordon wants to plant trees along the sides of his rectangular plot of land measuring 55 m by 30 m. Each tree is planted 5 m from the next. How many trees can he plant?

Challenging Problems

Worked Example 1

The figure shows a square made up of six rectangles. If the total perimeter of all six rectangles is 180 cm, find the area of the square.

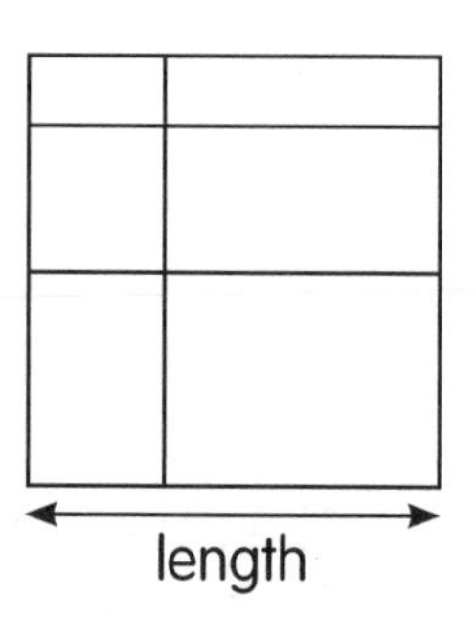

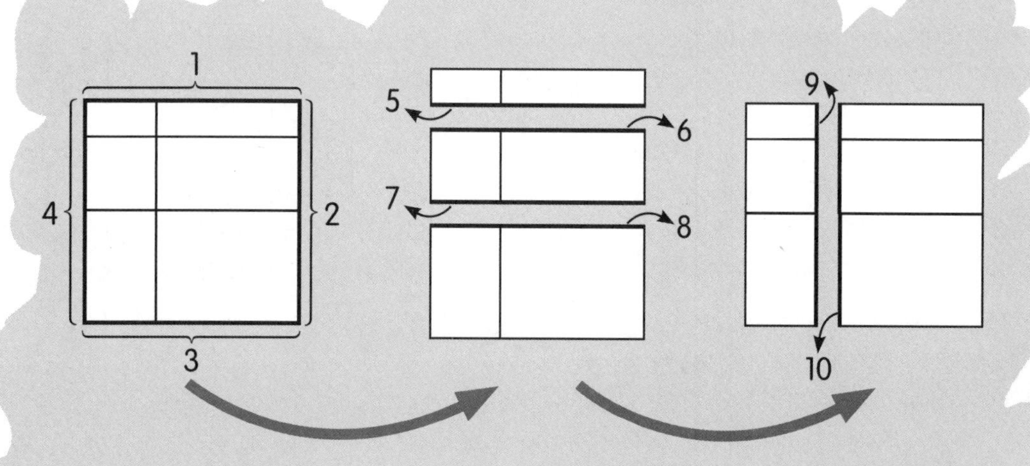

The figures above show 10 sides of the six rectangles.

Total perimeter of all rectangles = 10 × length of square

10 × length of square = 180 cm

Length of square = 180 cm ÷ 10
= 18 cm

Area = 18 cm × 18 cm
= 324 cm^2

The area of the square is **324 cm^2**.

Worked Example 2

A rectangular cardboard is 46 cm long and 27 cm wide. What is the maximum number of rectangles, each 7 cm long and 5 cm wide, which can be cut from it?

As shown below, the maximum number of rectangles that can be cut out is $(9 \times 3) + 6 = 33$. It will leave a strip of width 1 cm on the right and at the bottom, and a 5 cm long and 3 cm wide rectangle.

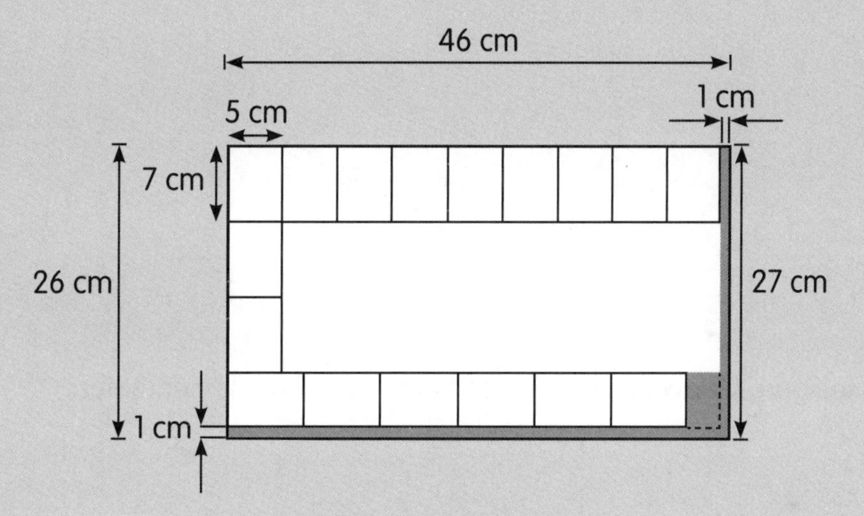

The maximum number of rectangles which can be cut from the rectangular cardboard is **33**.

Answer all questions.

1. The length of a rectangle is 8 cm longer than its width. If its perimeter is 84 cm, what is its area?

2. The figure below is made up of 2 squares. Find its perimeter.

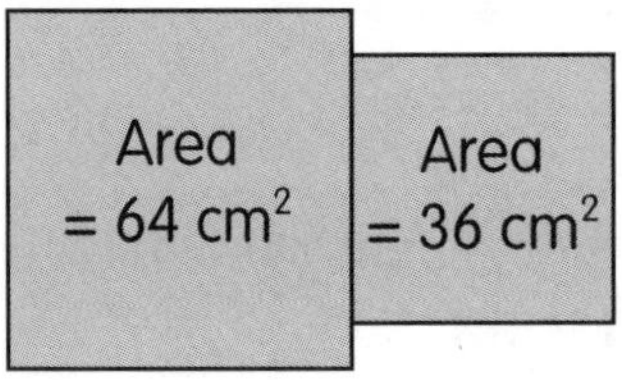

Area
= 64 cm^2

Area
= 36 cm^2

3. Carol wants to cut rectangles of length 5 cm and width 3 cm from a piece of paper. The piece of paper measures 12 cm by 8 cm. What is the maximum number of rectangles that she can cut from it?

4. A rectangular cardboard is 50 cm long and 27 cm wide. What is the maximum number of rectangles, each of length 8 cm and width 6 cm, that can be cut from it?

5. A square of sides 12 cm is divided by 2 lines into rectangles with areas of 20 cm^2, 28 cm^2, 40 cm^2, and 56 cm^2. Where should the lines divide the square?

5. The figure below is made up of 2 squares. The difference in their areas is 80 cm^2. If the sides of both squares are whole numbers, what is the perimeter of the figure?

7. Two rectangles have lengths 13 cm and 19 cm respectively. Their total area is 376 cm^2. If both their widths are whole numbers, what is the difference in their areas?

8. The figure below is made of 4 identical rectangles. The length of each rectangle is twice its width. The area of the figure is 200 cm^2. Find its perimeter.

9. The figure below shows two overlapping squares. What is the area of the shaded region?

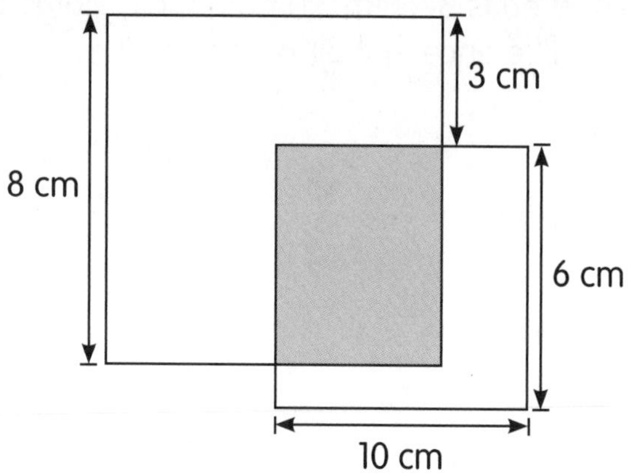

10. The figure below is made up of 13 identical rectangles. If its area is 520 cm^2, what is its perimeter?

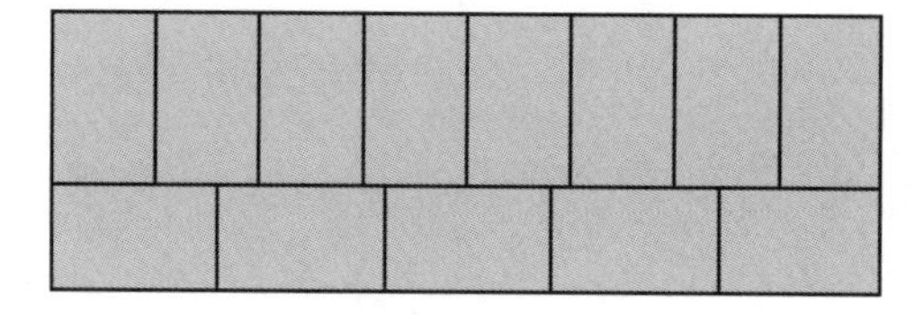

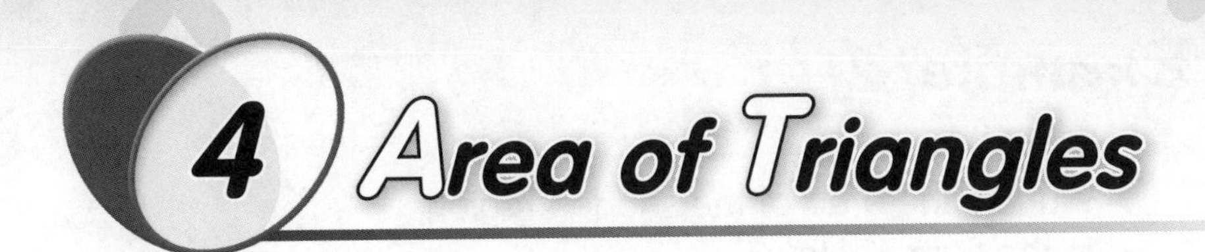

4 Area of Triangles

Worked Example 1

Find the area of the symmetrical figure below.

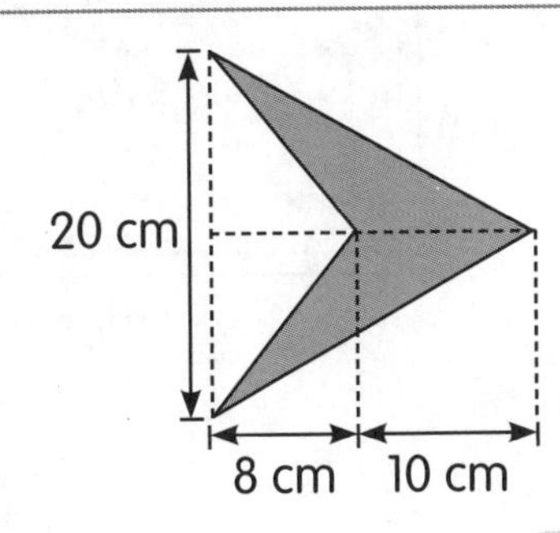

Method 1

Area of figure

= Area of triangle ABC
  − Area of triangle ADC

$= \frac{1}{2} \times AC \times BE - \frac{1}{2} \times AC \times DE$

$= \frac{1}{2} \times 20\text{ cm} \times (10\text{ cm} + 8\text{ cm}) - \frac{1}{2} \times 20\text{ cm} \times 8\text{ cm}$

$= 180\text{ cm}^2 - 80\text{ cm}^2$

$= 100\text{ cm}^2$

The area of the symmetrical figure is **100 cm²**.

Method 2

By symmetry, the area of triangle ABD is equal to the area of triangle CBD.

Area of figure $= 2 \times (\frac{1}{2} \times BD \times AE)$

$= 2 \times (\frac{1}{2} \times 10\text{ cm} \times 10\text{ cm})$

$= 100\text{ cm}^2$

The area of the symmetrical figure is **100 cm^2**.

Worked Example 2

What is the area of the shaded region in the figure below?

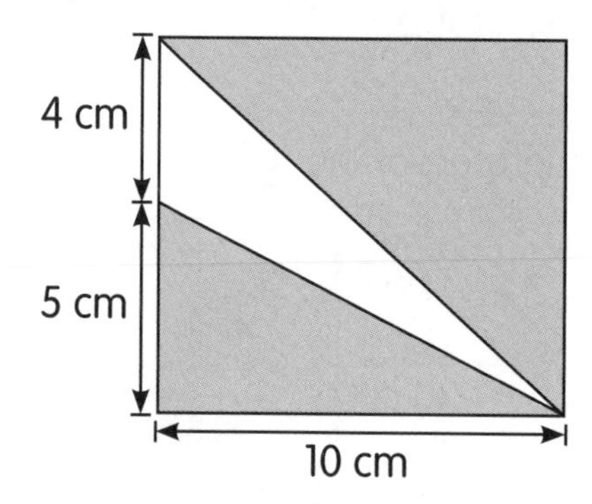

Method 1

Area of rectangle = 9 cm × 10 cm
= 90 cm^2

Area of unshaded triangle = $\frac{1}{2}$ × base × height
= $\frac{1}{2}$ × 4 cm × 10 cm
= 20 cm^2

Area of shaded region = 90 cm^2 – 20 cm^2
= 70 cm^2

The area of the shaded region is **70 cm^2**.

Method 2

The shaded region can be divided into two triangles, A and B.

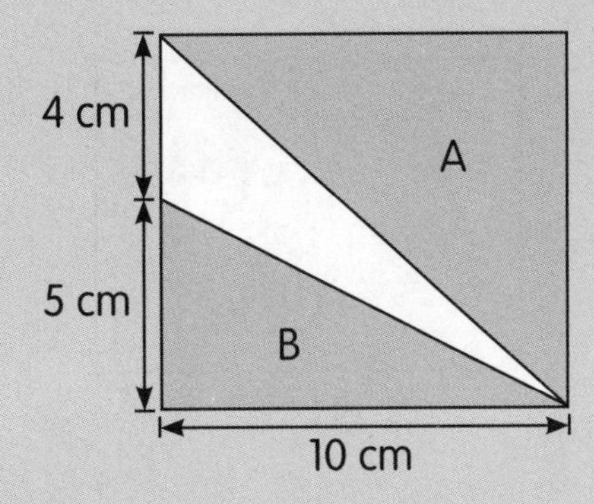

Area of Triangle A $= \frac{1}{2} \times 10\text{ cm} \times 9\text{ cm}$
$= 45\text{ cm}^2$

Area of Triangle B $= \frac{1}{2} \times 10\text{ cm} \times 5\text{ cm}$
$= 25\text{ cm}^2$

Area of shaded region $= 45\text{ cm}^2 + 25\text{ cm}^2$
$= 70\text{ cm}^2$

The area of the shaded region is **70 cm²**.

Worked Example 3

What is the area of the shaded region of the figure?

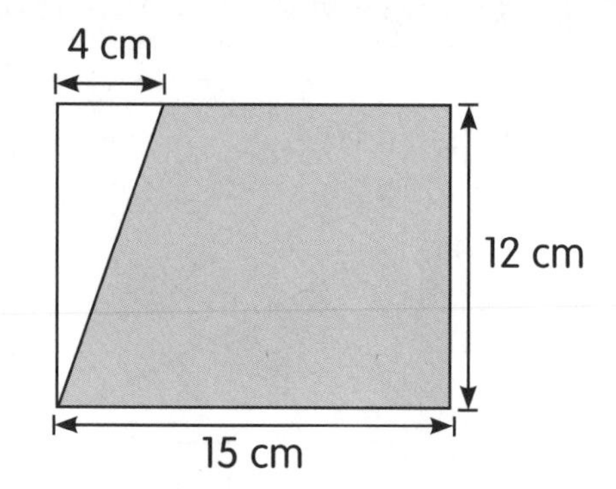

Method 1

Area of shaded region = Area of rectangle – Area of triangle

$= (15 \text{ cm} \times 12 \text{ cm}) - (\frac{1}{2} \times 4 \text{ cm} \times 12 \text{ cm})$

$= 180 \text{ cm}^2 - 24 \text{ cm}^2$

$= 156 \text{ cm}^2$

The area of the shaded region is **156 cm²**.

Method 2

Form a new rectangle by creating another identical shaded region.

Area of shaded region

$= \frac{1}{2} \times$ area of the new rectangle

$= \frac{1}{2} \times (15 \text{ cm} + 11 \text{ cm}) \times 12 \text{ cm}$

$= 156 \text{ cm}^2$

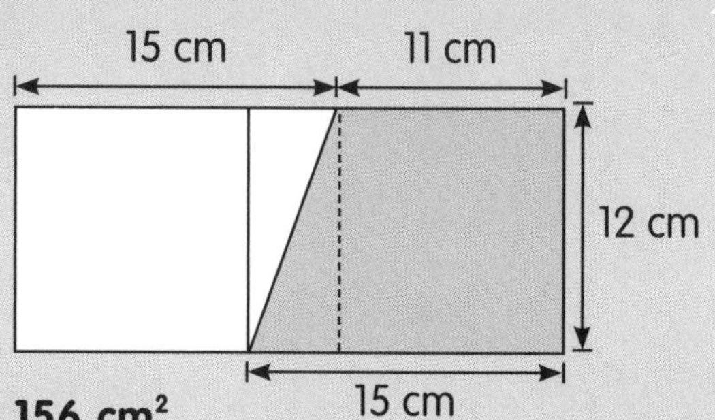

The area of the shaded region is **156 cm²**.

Method 3

Divide the shaded region into two triangles, A and B.

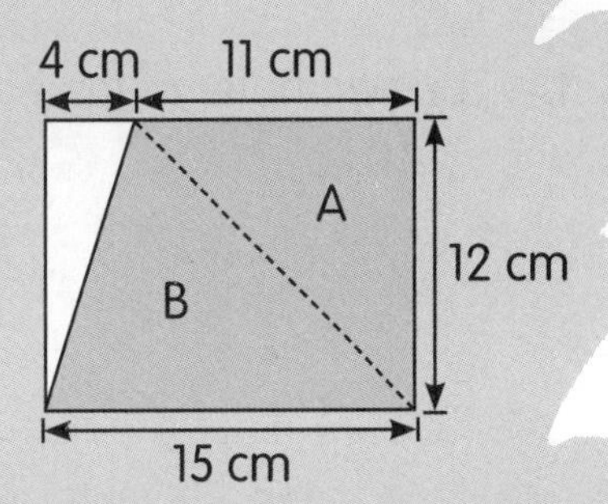

Area of shaded region
= Area of Triangle A + Area of Triangle B

$= (\frac{1}{2} \times 12\text{ cm} \times 11\text{ cm}) + (\frac{1}{2} \times 15\text{ cm} \times 12\text{ cm})$

$= 66\text{ cm}^2 + 90\text{ cm}^2$

$= 156\text{ cm}^2$

The area of the shaded region is **156 cm²**.

Method 4

Divide the shaded region into 2 triangles, P and Q.

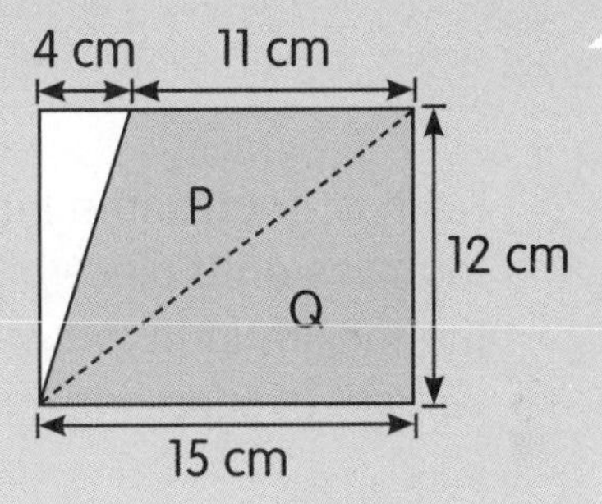

Area of shaded region
= Area of Triangle P + Area of Triangle Q

$= (\frac{1}{2} \times 11\text{ cm} \times 12\text{ cm}) + (\frac{1}{2} \times 15\text{ cm} \times 12\text{ cm})$

$= 66\text{ cm}^2 + 90\text{ cm}^2$

$= 156\text{ cm}^2$

The area of the shaded region is **156 cm²**.

Answer all questions.

1. The perimeter of the triangle below is 30 cm. What is its area?

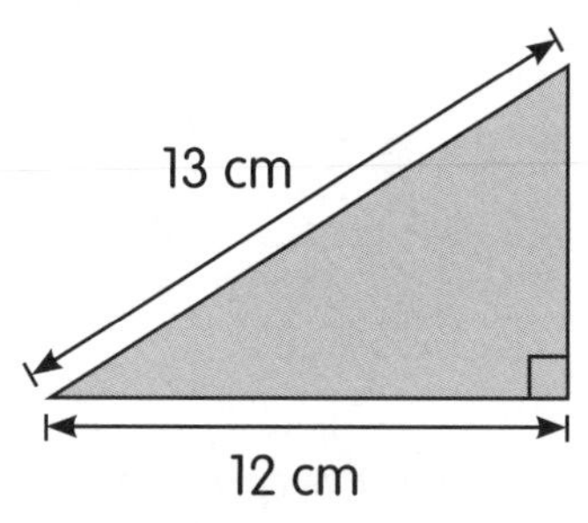

2 Keith is given some triangles as shown below. He needs to paste the triangles on a piece of paper of length 6 cm and width 4 cm. What is the maximum number of triangles that he can paste onto the paper without overlapping?

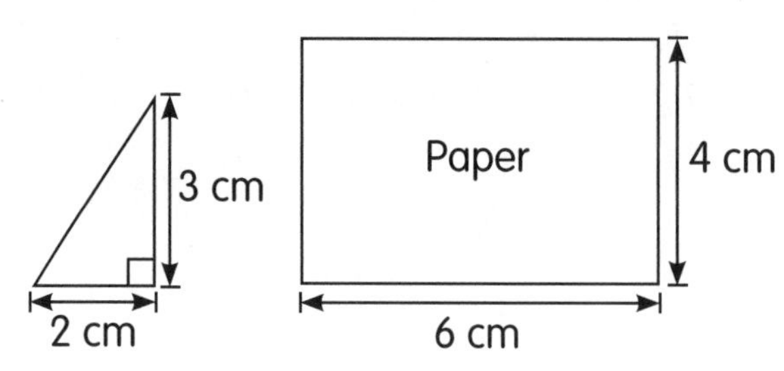

3. In the figure below, BD is parallel to AE. Show that triangles ABE, ACE, and ADE have the same area.

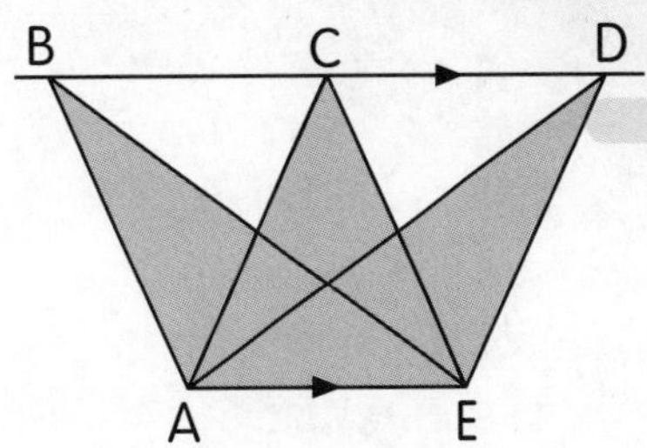

4. The figure below is symmetrical. What is its area?

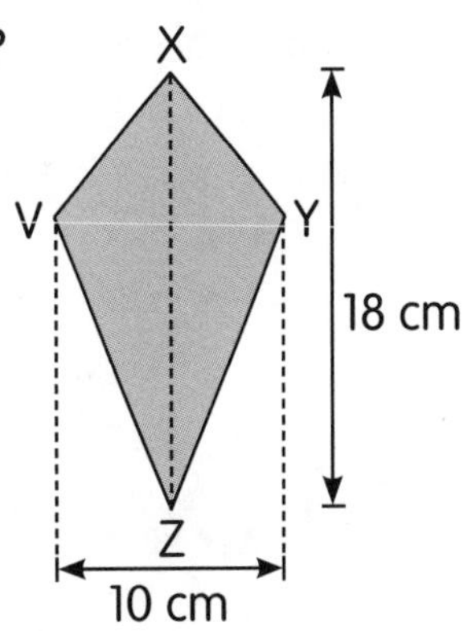

5. What is the area of the shaded region of the figure below?

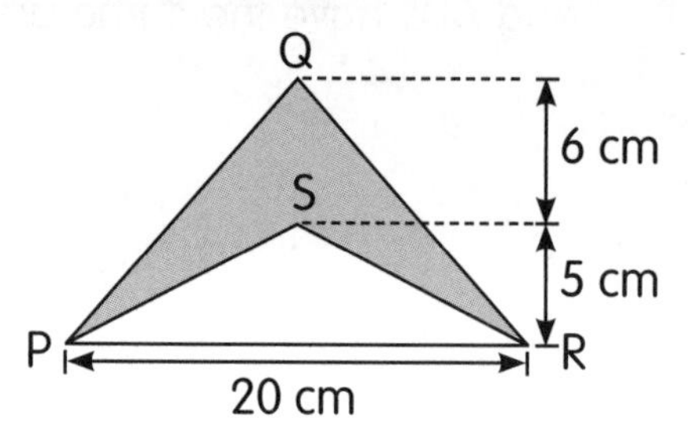

6. What is the area of the shaded region of the figure below?

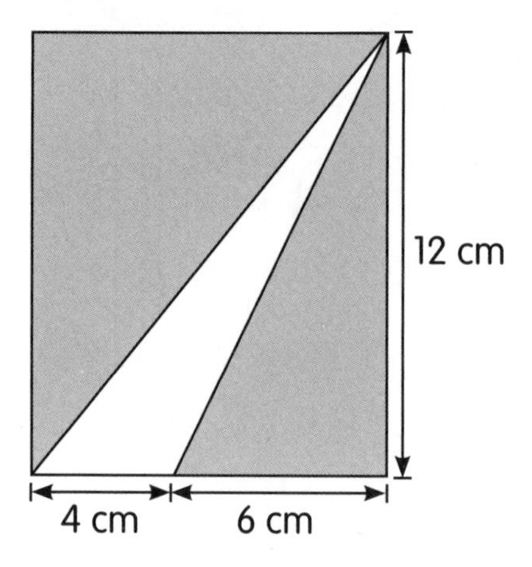

7. ABCD is a square of sides 17 cm. What is the area of the unshaded region?

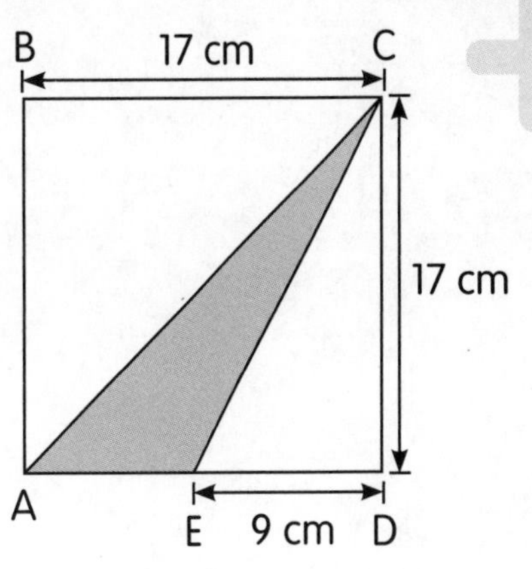

8. In the figure below, ABCD is a square of side 12 cm. E is the midpoint of BC and F is the midpoint of CD. What is the area of triangle AEF?

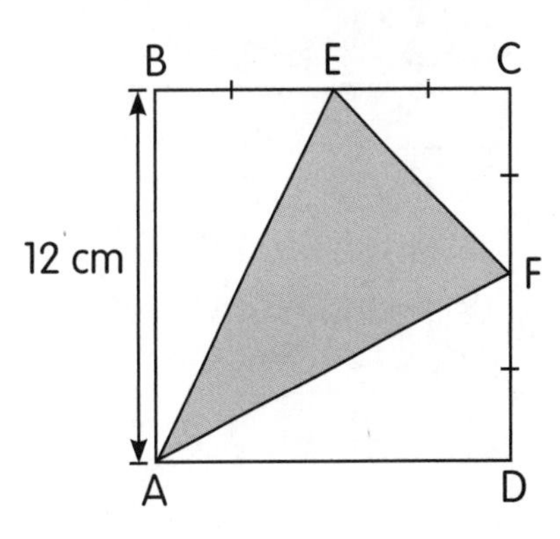

9. What is the area of the shaded region of the figure?

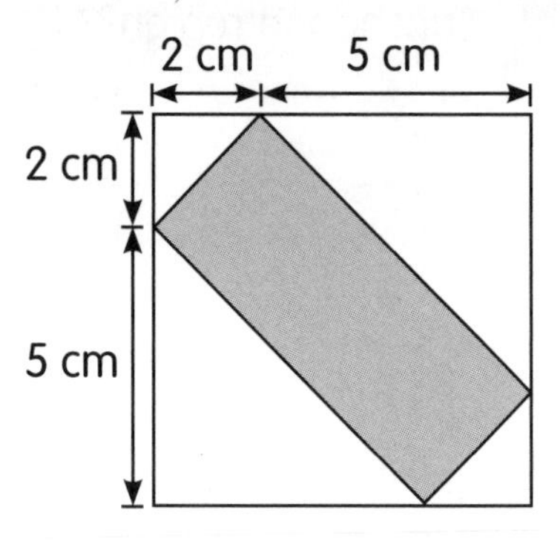

10. The figure below is made up of a rectangle and a triangle. What is the perimeter and the area of the figure?

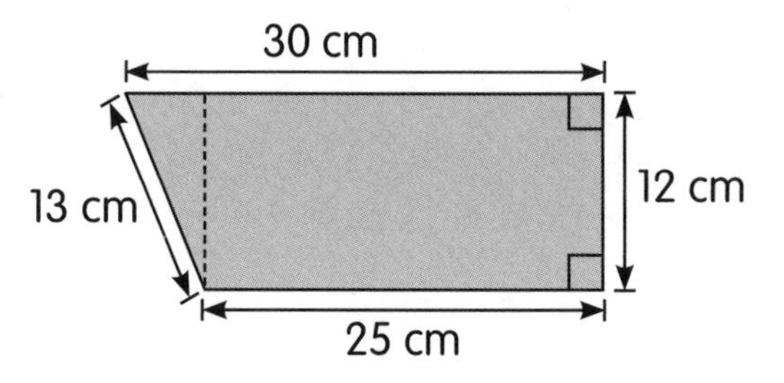

Challenging Problems

Worked Example 1

In the figure below, the length of square ABCG is 8 cm. The length of square GDEF is 12 cm. What is the area of the unshaded region?

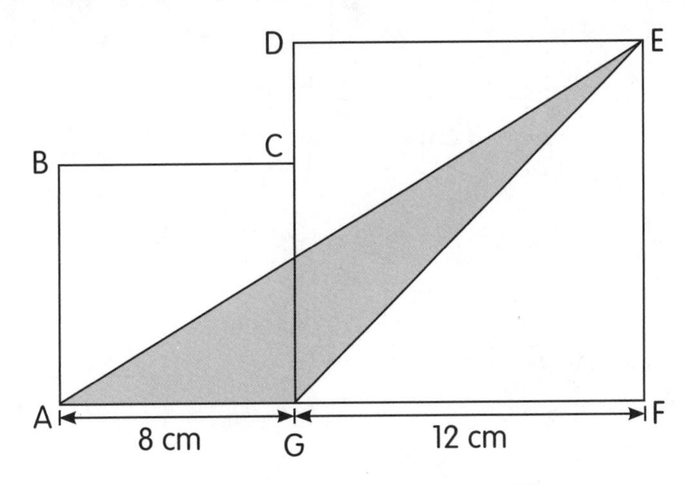

Area of triangle AEG $= \frac{1}{2} \times 8 \text{ cm} \times 12 \text{ cm}$

$= 48 \text{ cm}^2$

Area of unshaded region

= Area of square ABCG + Area of square GDEF – Area of triangle AEG

$= (8 \text{ cm} \times 8 \text{ cm}) + (12 \text{ cm} \times 12 \text{ cm}) - 48 \text{ cm}^2$

$= 64 \text{ cm}^2 + 144 \text{ cm}^2 - 48 \text{ cm}^2$

$= 160 \text{ cm}^2$

The area of the unshaded region is **160 cm^2**.

Worked Example 2

The length of Square A is 8 cm. The length of Square B is 6 cm. Squares A and B overlap each other. What is the difference in the areas of the two unshaded regions?

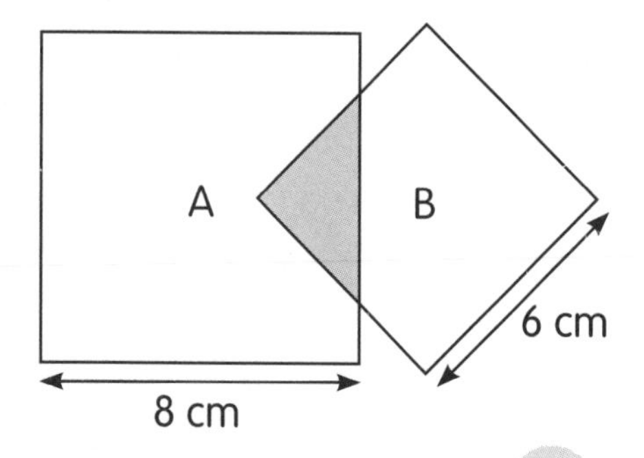

Case 1:

If Squares A and B do not overlap each other, the difference in areas

$= (8\text{ cm} \times 8\text{ cm}) - (6\text{ cm} \times 6\text{ cm})$

$= 64\text{ cm}^2 - 36\text{ cm}^2$

$= 28\text{ cm}^2$

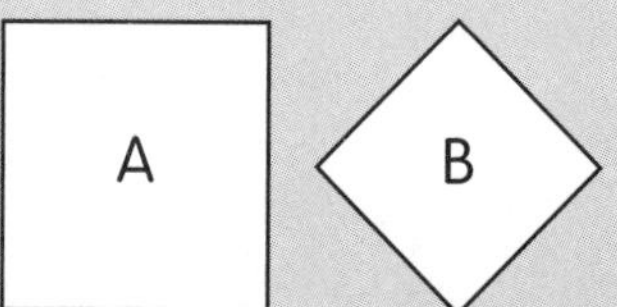

Case 2:

If Square B is inside Square A, the difference in areas

$= (8\text{ cm} \times 8\text{ cm}) - (6\text{ cm} \times 6\text{ cm})$

$= 64\text{ cm}^2 - 36\text{ cm}^2$

$= 28\text{ cm}^2$

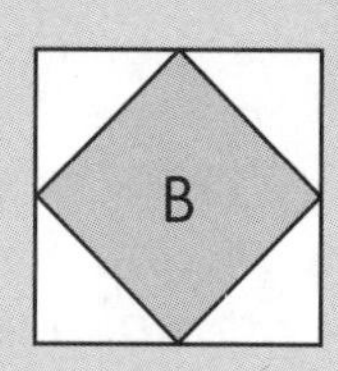

Case 3:

If half of Square B overlaps Square A, the difference in areas

$= (8\text{ cm} \times 8\text{ cm} - \frac{1}{2} \times 6\text{ cm} \times 6\text{ cm}) - (\frac{1}{2} \times 6\text{ cm} \times 6\text{ cm})$

$= (64\text{ cm}^2 - 18\text{ cm}^2) - 18\text{ cm}^2$

$= 28\text{ cm}^2$

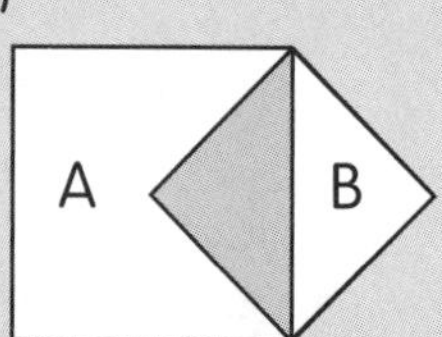

The above three cases show that regardless of how the squares are overlapped, the difference in the areas of the two unshaded regions is always **28 cm²**.

Answer all questions.

1. The length of square ABCG is 8 cm. The length of square GDEF is 6 cm. What is the area of the shaded region?

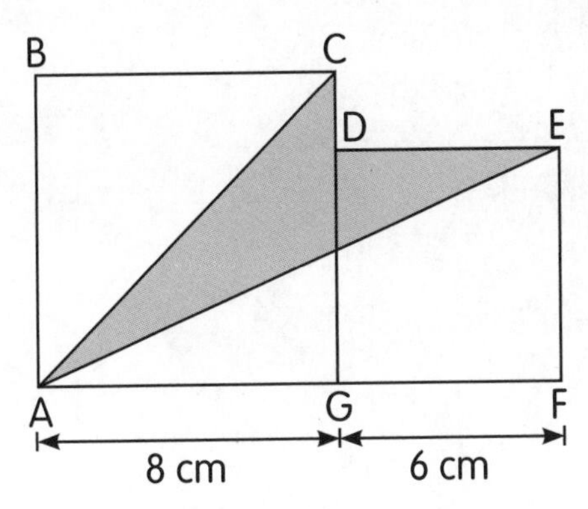

2. The diagonal of the square figure below is 10 cm. Find its area.

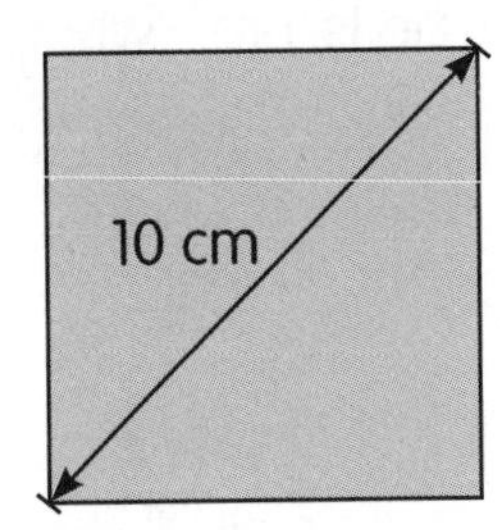

3. The figure below is formed by overlapping two identical squares. The overlapping area is $\frac{1}{4}$ of the area of each square. What fraction of the figure is shaded?

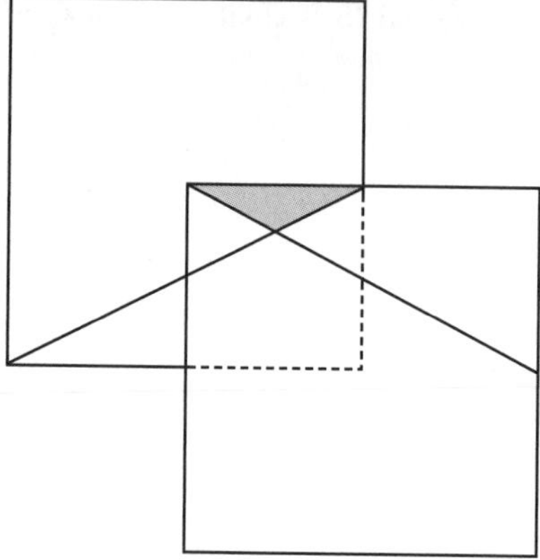

4. The figure below shows a square puzzle made up of seven shapes. If the area of the square puzzle is 1 m^2, what is the area of each shape?

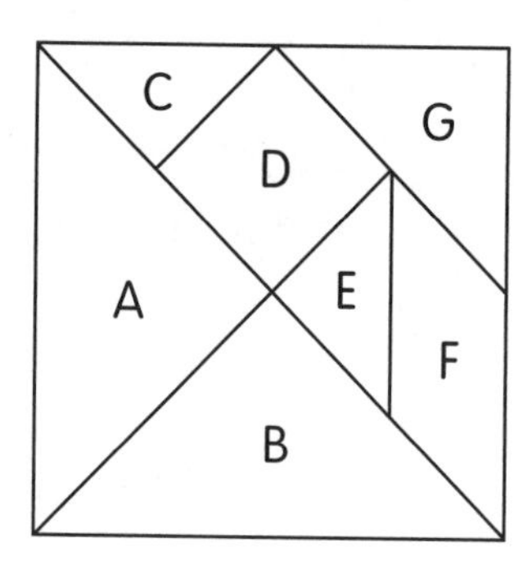

5. The figure below shows two equilateral triangles ABD, and CDE. AB is parallel to EC. The height of equilateral triangle CDE is $\frac{1}{4}$ of the height of equilateral triangle ABD. What fraction of the equilateral triangle ABD is shaded?

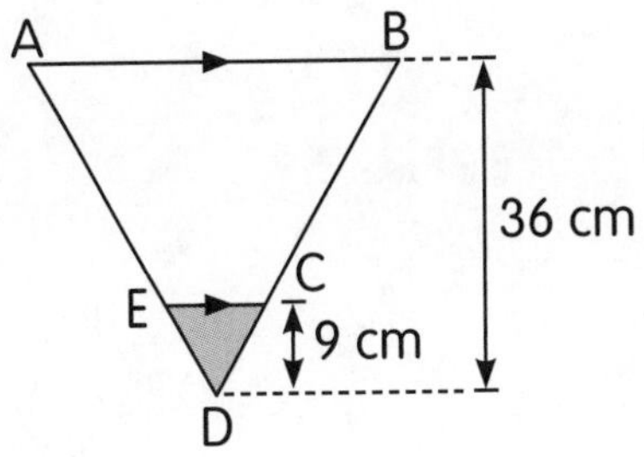

6. In the figure below, AJ = JI = IH = HG, and BC = CD = DE = EF. What fraction of the figure is shaded?

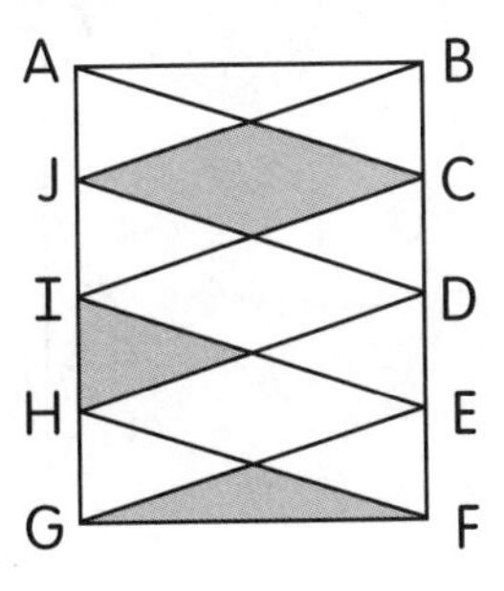

7. The length of square PQUV is 10 cm. The length of square RSTU is 6 cm. Find the area of the shaded region.

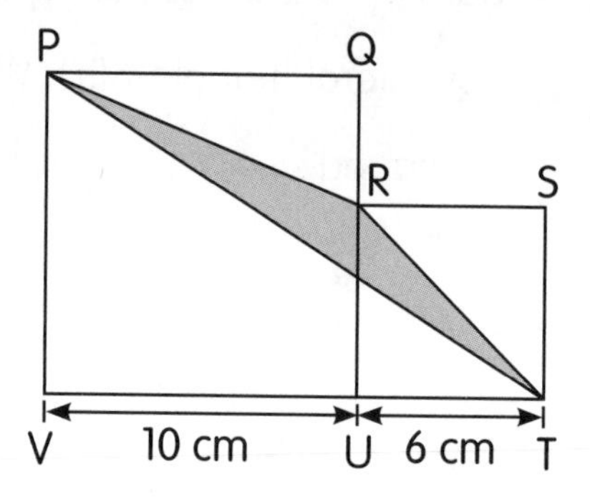

8. Rectangle ABCD is divided into four triangles. Triangle AED has an area of 16 cm^2, triangle DEC has an area of 25 cm^2, and triangle EBC has an area of 24 cm^2. Find the area of triangle ABE.

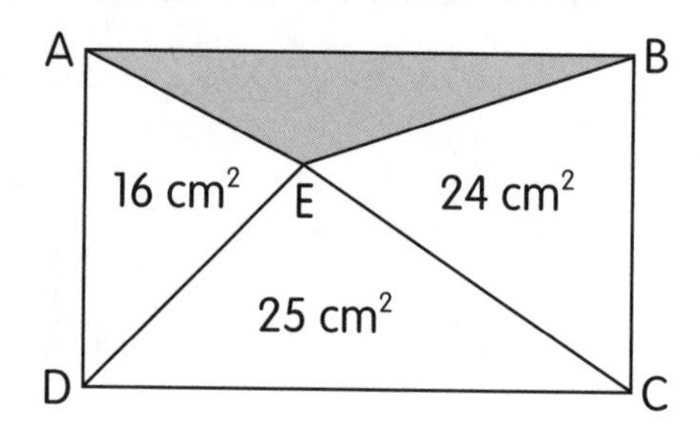

9. PQRS is a square of side 24 cm. If PX = $\frac{1}{3}$ XS and QY = $\frac{1}{4}$ QR, what is the area of the shaded region?

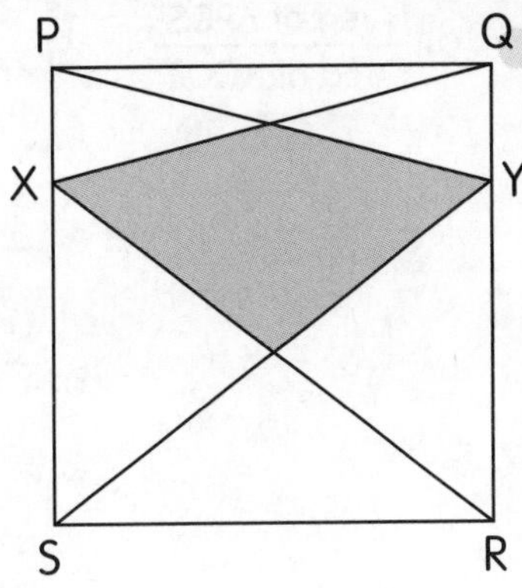

10. In the figure below, the lines AC and BD meet at O.
If OA = 50 cm, OB = 40 cm, OC = 60 cm, and OD = 48 cm, find the value of $\frac{\text{Area of } \Delta OAB}{\text{Area of } \Delta OCD}$.

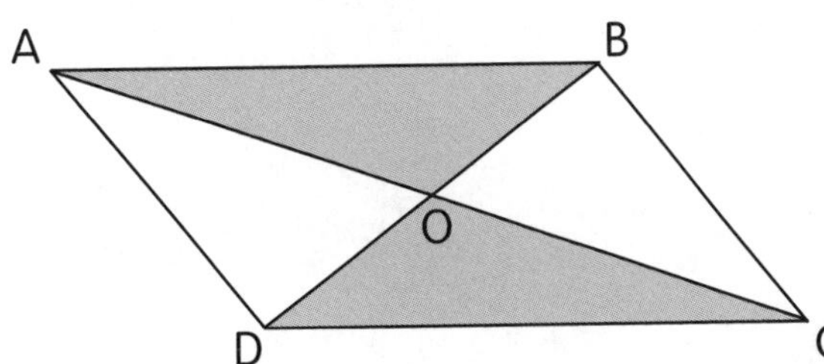

11. In the figure below, the lines PR and QS meet at point O.
If PO = 4 cm, QO = 5 cm, RO = 6 cm, and SO = 7.5 cm, find the value of $\frac{\text{Area of } \Delta POS}{\text{Area of } \Delta QOR}$.

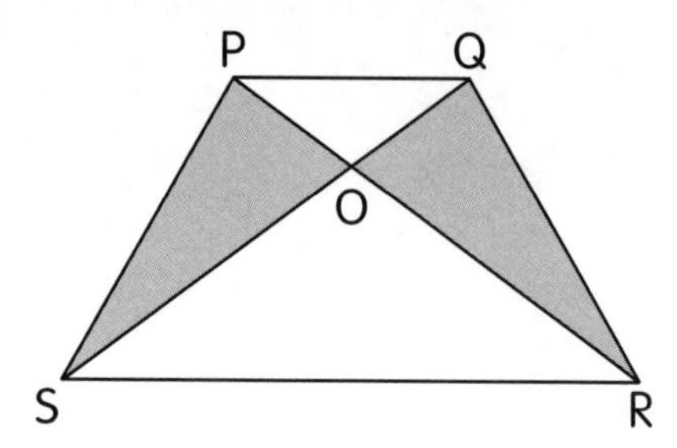

5 Ratio

Worked Example 1

The ratio of the number of Joel's stickers to the number of Tony's stickers is 3 : 5. Joel has 36 stickers. How many stickers does Tony have?

36

Joel [ ][ ][ ]

Tony [ ][ ][ ][ ][ ]

?

3 units ⟶ 36
1 unit ⟶ $36 \div 3 = 12$
5 units ⟶ $5 \times 12 = 60$

Tony has **60** stickers.

Worked Example 2

The ratio of the number of boys to the number of girls in a class is 5 : 3. There are 8 more boys than girls. How many students are there in the class?

Boys
Girls
?
8

2 units ⟶ 8
1 unit ⟶ $8 \div 2 = 4$
8 units ⟶ $8 \times 4 = 32$

There are **32** students in the class.

Worked Example 3

The ratio of the number of Cindy's stickers to the number of Roy's stickers is 4 : 7. If Cindy gives $\frac{1}{8}$ of her stickers to Roy, what will be the new ratio of the number of Cindy's stickers to the number of Roy's stickers?

Number of Cindy's stickers	:	Number of Roy's stickers
= 4	:	7
= 8	:	14

Cindy

Roy

The new ratio of the number of Cindy's stickers to the number of Roy's stickers is **7 : 15**.

Answer all questions.

1. The ratio of the number of Kate's marbles to the number of Peter's marbles is 5 : 6. Peter has 24 marbles. How many marbles does Kate have?

2. The ratio of the number of men to the number of women in a room is 7 : 4. There are 9 more men than women. How many people are there in the room?

3. A students' club has 60 members. The ratio of the number of boys to the number of girls is 7 : 5. How many more boys than girls are there in the club?

4. The ratio of the number of Mike's envelopes to the number of Doris's envelopes is 3 : 7. If Mike gives $\frac{1}{6}$ of his envelopes to Doris, what will be the new ratio of the number of Mike's envelopes to the number of Doris's envelopes?

5. The ratio of the number of Esther's cards to the number of Andy's cards is 5 : 8. If Esther gives $\frac{3}{10}$ of her cards to Andy, what will be the new ratio of the number of Esther's cards to the number of Andy's cards?

6. The ratio of the number of Daniel's coins to the number of Mary's coins is 9 : 13. If Mary has 52 coins, how many coins do they have altogether?

7. Mark bought some oranges, pineapples, and apples. The ratio of the weight of the oranges to the weight of the pineapples was 4 : 7. The weight of the apples was $\frac{5}{11}$ of the total weight of the fruits. The pineapples weighed 18 kg more than the oranges. What was the total weight of the fruits?

8. The ratio of the ages of Jay, Tim, and Angela now is 3 : 7 : 9. 10 years ago, Tim was 25 years old. What will be the ratio of their ages in 5 years' time?

9. Joyce had $75 and Leslie had $48. After each spent the same amount of money, the ratio of the amount of money Joyce had to the amount of money Leslie had was 7 : 4. How much did each of them have left?

10. Sally had 48 stickers. The ratio of the number of Sally's stickers to the number of Eric's stickers was 4 : 7. Sally then bought another 8 stickers. What is the new ratio of the number of Sally's stickers to the number of Eric's stickers ?

11. Henry and Grace had the same amount of money. After Henry spent $28 and Grace spent $16, the ratio of the amount of money Henry had to the amount of money Grace had was 2 : 5. How much money did each of them have at first?

Challenging Problems

Worked Example 1

The ratio of Ann's money to Jean's money was 4 : 7. After Ann spent half of her money and Jean spent $45, Jean had twice as much money as Ann. How much money did Ann have at first?

Before

Ann

Jean

After

$45

Ann

Jean

3 units ⟶ $45
1 unit ⟶ $45 ÷ 3 = $15
4 units ⟶ 4 × $15 = $60

Ann had **$60** at first.

Worked Example 2

Gary had some 50¢ and $1 coins. The ratio of the number of 50¢ coins to the number of $1 coins was 2 : 3. After Gary received more 50¢ and $1 coins from his father, the ratio became 1 : 3. The total value of his 50¢ coins in the end was $10. How many $1 coins did Gary receive from his father if he had eighteen 50¢ coins at first?

50¢ coins : $1 coins

$$\times 9 \quad 2 : 3 \quad \times 9$$
$$18 : 27$$

Gary had twenty-seven $1 coins at first.

$10 = 1000¢
1000¢ ÷ 50¢ = 20

Gary has twenty 50¢ coins now.

50¢ coins : $1 coins

$$\times 20 \quad 1 : 3 \quad \times 20$$
$$20 : 60$$

Gary has sixty $1 coins now.

$60 - 27 = 33$

Gary received **thirty-three** $1 coins from his father.

Answer all questions.

1. The ratio of the amount of money Terry had to the amount of money Maria had was 4 : 9. After Terry spent half of his money and Maria spent $20, Maria had twice as much money as Terry. How much money did Terry have at first?

2. The ratio of the number of Michael's books to the number of Janet's books was 4 : 5. After Michael received another 24 books, he had twice as many books as Janet. How many books did Michael have at first?

3. The ratio of the number of Adrian's crayons to the number of Susan's crayons was 3 : 5. After Susan gave 21 crayons to her cousin, she had half as many crayons as Adrian. How many crayons did Adrian have at first?

4. The ratio of the amount of money Elaine had to the amount of money Lynn had was 5 : 9. After Elaine spent half of her money and Lynn spent $15, Lynn had three times as much money as Elaine. How much money did Elaine have at first?

5. In a school, the ratio of the number of boys to the number of girls is 8 : 5. $\frac{1}{4}$ of the boys and $\frac{1}{15}$ of the girls wear glasses. When another 48 students who wear glasses join the school, the total number of students who wear glasses in the school becomes 216. How many boys wear glasses?

6. The ratio of the number of Joe's marbles to the number of Fred's marbles was 8 : 3. After Joe gave 15 marbles to Fred, they each had the same number of marbles. How many marbles did Joe have at first?

7. The ratio of the number of men to the number of women registered for a marathon was 17 : 15. 90 fewer men and 80 fewer women turned up for the marathon. The ratio of the number of men to the number of women became 8 : 7. How many people registered for the marathon?

8. In a school, the ratio of the number of boys to the number of girls is 2 : 3 and the ratio of the number of girls to the number of teachers is 7 : 4. What is the ratio of the number of students to the number of teachers?

9. The ratio of the number of David's cards to the number of Tom's cards is 4 : 5. The ratio of the number of Tom's cards to the number of Jack's cards is 7 : 8. If Jack has 24 more cards than David, how many cards does Tom have?

10. Five gold coins can be balanced by a weight. Four silver coins can also balance the same weight. How many silver coins with twenty gold coins are required to balance ten similar weights?

6 Decimals

Worked Example 1

Without calculating the answers, explain why (a) and (b) will have the same answer.

(a) $0.12\overline{)5.6}$ (b) $12\overline{)560}$

Method 1

When we shift the decimal points of 0.12 and 5.6 two places to the right, we multiply the numbers by 100.

$$\begin{aligned} 5.6 \div 0.12 &= (5.6 \times 100) \div (0.12 \times 100) \\ &= 560 \div 12 \end{aligned}$$

Therefore, (a) and (b) will have the same answer.

Method 2

Interpret 5.6 ÷ 0.12 as, "How many groups of \$0.12 can you get from \$5.60?"

If we convert dollars to cents, the question becomes "How many groups of 12 cents can you get from 560 cents?", which we can solve by dividing 12 from 560.

Therefore, (a) and (b) will have the same answer.

Worked Example 2

Emily bought 32.8 m of cloth to make 6 shirts and 2 pairs of pants. She used 3.25 m of cloth for each shirt and the remaining cloth for the pants. How much cloth did she use for each pair of pants?

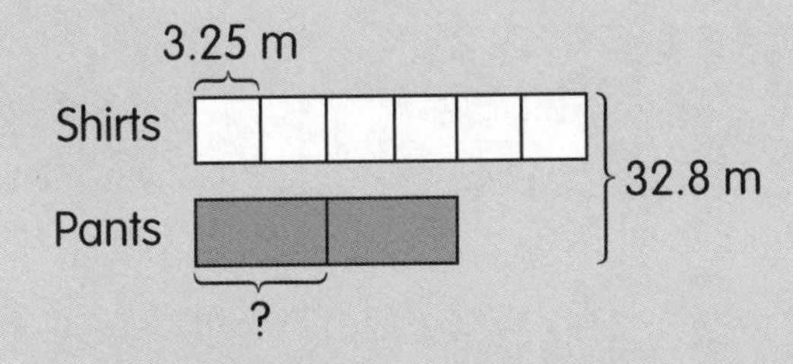

Length of cloth to make 6 shirts = 6×3.25 m
= 19.5 m

Length of cloth to make 2 pairs of pants
= 32.8 m – 19.5 m
= 13.3 m

Length of cloth to make 1 pair of pants
= 13.3 m ÷ 2
= 6.65 m

She used **6.65 m** of cloth for each pair of pants.

Worked Example 3

Two wallets and four caps cost $67.90.
Five wallets and nine caps cost $160.25.
What is the cost of one cap?

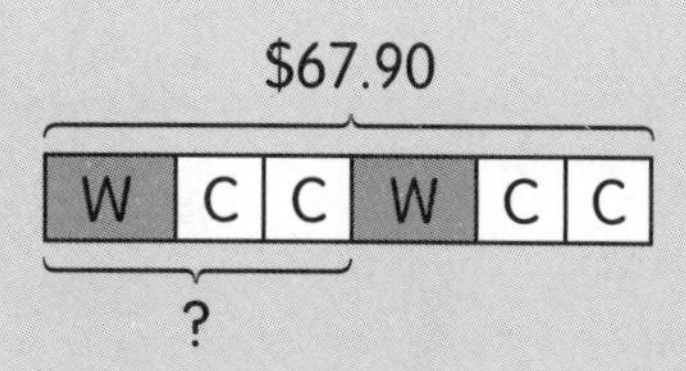

2 wallets + 4 caps = $67.90
1 wallet + 2 caps = $67.90 ÷ 2
= $33.95

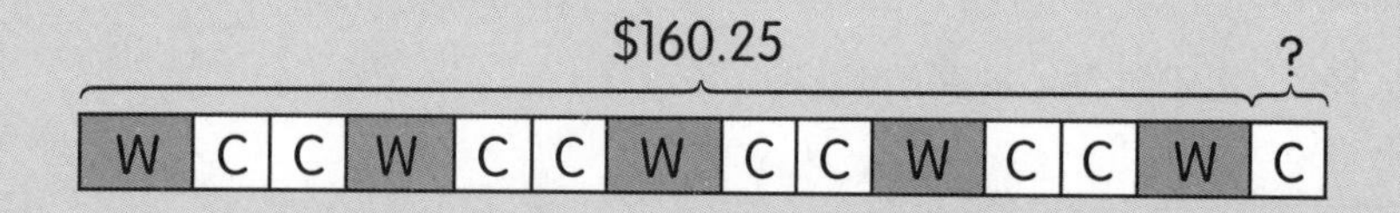

5 wallets + 10 caps = 5 × $33.95
= $169.75
5 wallets + 9 caps = $160.25 (given)
1 cap = $169.75 – $160.25
= $9.50

The cost of one cap is **$9.50**.

Practice Questions

Answer all questions.

1. Given that $4.85 \times 3.24 = 15.714$, find the value of the following:
   (a) $157.14 \div 0.00324$
   (b) $0.015714 \div 485$
   (c) 0.0324×4850

2. James mixed 0.125 l of Syrup A with 0.375 l of Syrup B and 0.25 l of Syrup C. What is the volume of the mixture?

3. Ryan bought a hard drive for $74.95 and a thumb drive for $23.50. He gave the cashier a $100 bill. How much change did he receive?

4. Arthur bought 7 pens for $1.32 each. He gave the cashier a $20 bill. How much change did he receive?

5. A bottle holds 6 ounces of cough syrup. If May needs to drink 0.4 ounces of cough syrup each day, in how many days will she finish it?

6. If a bunch of grapes costs $1.35 per kg, what fraction of a kilogram of grapes can you buy with $0.45?

7. Mr. Charles bought 8 notebooks, 8 files, 8 watches, and 9 balls. How much did he spend altogether?

Item	Cost
Notebook	$2.45
File	$4.25
Ball	$12.50
Watch	$14.95

8. The difference between Alex's and Cathy's height is the same as the difference between Cathy's and Denise's height. Alex is 1.52 m tall and Cathy is 1.23 m tall. If Denise is shorter than Cathy, find Denise's height.

9. Roger had $1200. He bought a phone with 0.4 of the money and a helmet with 0.5 of the remaining money. What is the amount of money Roger had left?

10. Laurel and Harry worked 5 h each. They earned $120 in all. If Laurel earned $0.60 more than Harry per hour, how much did Laurel earn per hour?

11. Bag A contained 3 times the weight of sand in Bag B. After 6.25 kg of sand were removed from Bag A and 1.4 kg were removed from Bag B, Bag B contained 0.35 kg more sand than Bag A. What was the new weight of sand in Bag B?

Challenging Problems

Worked Example 1

In the recurring decimal 0.12345 12345 12345..., what is the 2013th digit to the right of the decimal point?

Notice that the pattern of 5 digits, 12345, repeats itself in the decimal.

$$\begin{aligned} 2013 &= 5 \times 402 + 3 \\ &= 2010 + 3 \end{aligned}$$

Since 2013 is 3 more than 2010, which is a multiple of 5, the 2013th digit will be the 3rd digit to the right of 5. The 2013th digit is **3**.

Worked Example 2

Two calculators and four batteries cost $33. Three calculators and two batteries cost $40.50. What is the cost of one battery?

Calculators
Batteries
$33

Calculators
Batteries
$40.50

Method 1

Cost of 6 calculators and 4 batteries = $40.50 × 2
= $81

Cost of 4 calculators = $81 – $33
= $48

Cost of 2 calculators = $48 ÷ 2
= $24

Cost of 4 batteries = $33 – $24
= $9

Cost of 1 battery = $9 ÷ 4
= $2.25

The cost of one battery is **$2.25**.

Method 2

Cost of 1 calculator and 2 batteries = $33 ÷ 2
= $16.50

Cost of 2 calculators = $40.50 – $16.50
= $24

Cost of 4 batteries = $33 – $24
= $9

Cost of 1 battery = $9 ÷ 4
= $2.25

The cost of one battery is **$2.25**.

Answer all questions.

1. Jeffrey multiplies a number by itself and then adds 10. His answer is 23.69. What is the number?

2. In the recurring decimal 0.053412 053412..., what is the 50th digit to the right of the decimal point?

3. When the fraction $\frac{3}{7}$ is expressed in decimal form, which digit is in the 21st decimal place?

4. Anita has $42.55 worth of coins in her piggy bank. The coins are in denominations of 5¢, 10¢, 20¢, 50¢, and $1. If there are an equal number of coins for each denomination, how many coins are there in all?

5. Sam bought 15 pies and 7 slices of cake for $55.25. If each pie costs $\frac{2}{5}$ as much as a slice of cake, what was the total cost of 1 pie and 2 slices of cake?

6. The total weight of Robbie and a trophy is 69.95 kg. The total weight of Sarah and the same trophy is 63.1 kg. If Robbie and Sarah weigh 116.05 kg in all, find the weight of
   (a) the trophy.
   (b) Robbie.
   (c) Sarah.

7. The volume of water in Tank B was 3 times the volume of water in Tank A. After Hilda poured 0.45 l of water into Tank A and another 12.75 l of water into Tank B, the volume of water in Tank B became 5 times the volume of water in Tank A. What was the initial volume of water in Tank B?

8. Alvin saved a portion of his daily pocket money. Each day, he saved $1.40 more than the previous day. At the end of one week, he had saved $36.40. How much did he save on the third day?

9. Paul and Ian had a total of $63. After Paul gave 0.3 of his money to Ian, Ian gave $\frac{1}{3}$ of his total amount of money to Calvin. If all three boys had the same amount of money in the end, how much did Paul have at first?

10. A transport company delivered 78 plates to a shop. It charged $1.50 for every plate delivered. It had to compensate $9.50 for every broken plate. If the company collected $73 from the shop owner, how many plates were broken?

11. A whole number, N, lies between 35 and 45. When N is multiplied by 0.45, the product is another whole number. Find the value of N.

7 Volume

Worked Example 1

24 unit cubes are used to form a rectangular prism. How many different rectangular prisms can be formed using all 24 unit cubes?

The factors of 24 are 1, 2, 3, 4, 6, 8, 12, and 24.

Look for three factors with a product of 24.

Number of possible dimensions of the rectangular prism:

$1 \times 1 \times 24$
$1 \times 2 \times 12$
$1 \times 3 \times 8$
$1 \times 4 \times 6$
$2 \times 2 \times 6$
$2 \times 4 \times 3$

Six different rectangular prisms can be formed.

Worked Example 2

Pitcher A contained the same volume of water as Pitcher B. After 445 ml of water was poured out from Pitcher A and 65 ml of water was poured out from Pitcher B, the volume of water in Pitcher B was five times the volume of water in Pitcher A. What was the volume of water in each pitcher at first?

4 units ⟶ 445 ml – 65 ml = 380 ml
1 unit ⟶ 380 ml ÷ 4 = 95 ml

95 ml + 445 ml = 540 ml

The volume of water in each pitcher at first was **540 ml**.

Answer all questions.

1. The rectangular prism below has a volume of $\frac{1}{4}$ m^3. What is its length?

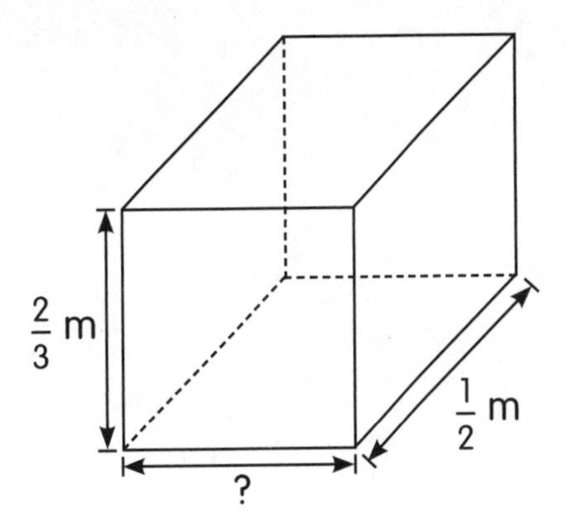

2. The width of a rectangular block is 16 cm. It is half as wide as its length. The width is four times its height. What is the volume of the block?

3. A tank, measuring 22 m by 18 m by 12 m, is filled with water to a depth of 7 m. When more water is added to the tank, the height of the water level becomes 10.8 m. How much water is added?

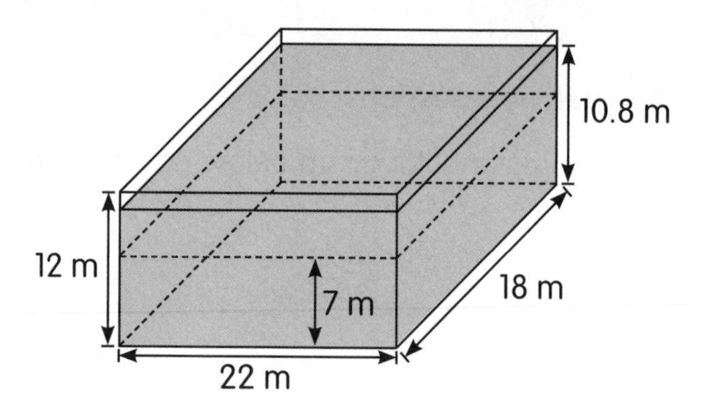

4. The figure below shows a tank. How much more water is required to fill the tank completely? Give your answer in liters and milliliters.
(1 l = 1000 cm^3)

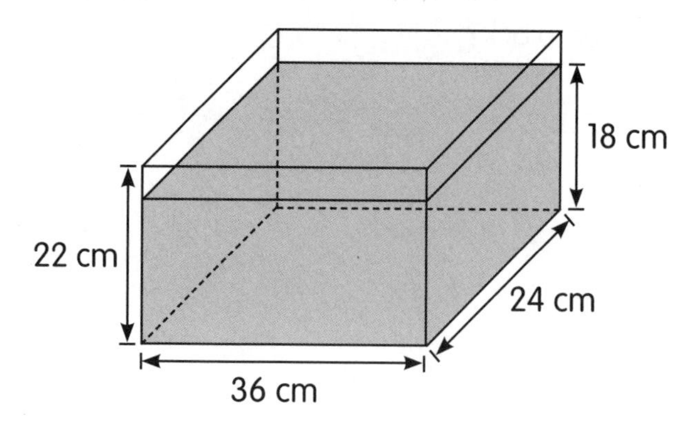

5. A container, measuring 38 cm by 30 cm by 18 cm, is $\frac{3}{5}$-filled with water. How much more water is required to fill the tank completely? Give your answer in liters and milliliters. (1 l = 1000 cm^3)

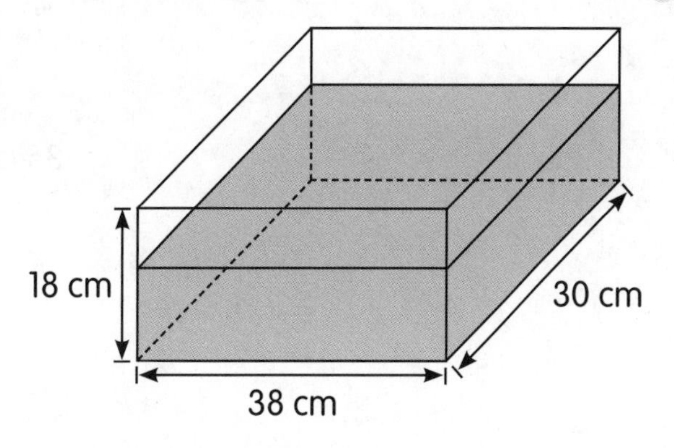

6. A wooden block measures 48 cm by 36 cm by 28 cm. A 4-cm cube is cut away from each of its corners. What is the volume of the remaining block?

7. A tank, measuring 60 cm by 55 cm by 35 cm, was filled with water to its brim. If 29.7 l of the water were poured out from the tank, what was the height of the water level in the end?

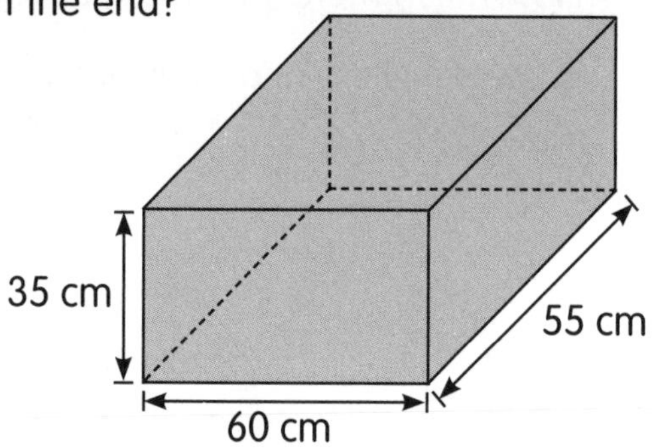

8. A rectangular tank, measuring 1 m by 80 cm by 60 cm, contained 140 l of water. When more water was added into the tank, the total volume of water increased to 210 l. Find the increase in the water level.

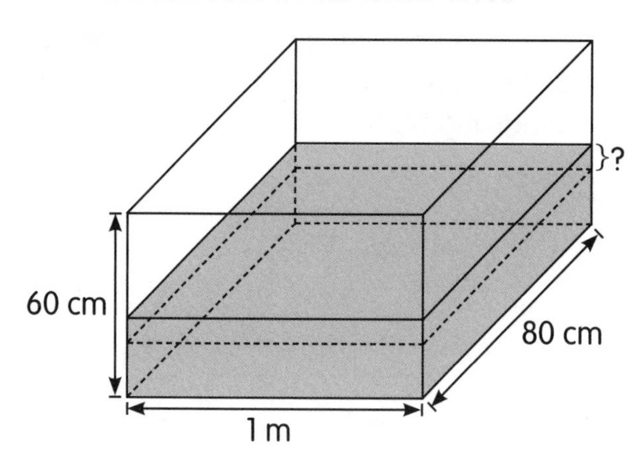

9. A piece of square cardboard measures 10 cm by 10 cm. A box can be formed by cutting out identical squares from each corner and folding up the sides. Find the volume of the box formed when
   (a) 1-cm squares are cut out.
   (b) 2-cm squares are cut out.
   (c) 3-cm squares are cut out.

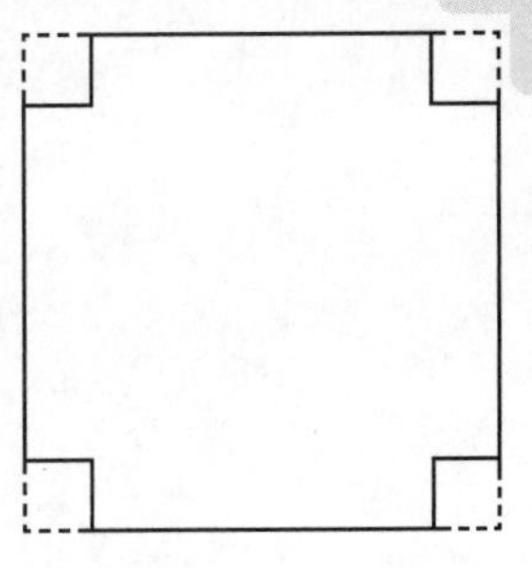

10. The total capacity of three tanks P, Q, and R is 522 *l*. The capacity of Tank P is 30 *l* more than Tank Q. The capacity of Tank R is 4 times as much as the capacity Tank Q. Find the capacity of Tank P.

11. In the figure below, the container is filled with water to a depth of 10 cm. What is the volume of water?

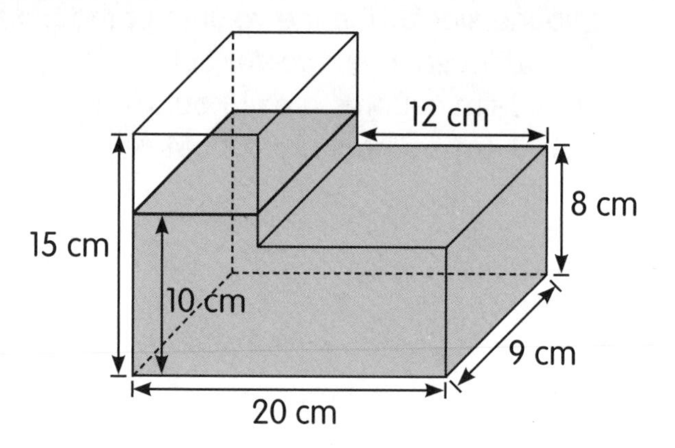

Worked Example 1

When 6 identical cubes were placed in a measuring beaker containing some water, the total volume of the water and the cubes was 850 ml. When 2 cubes were removed, the total volume decreased to 700 ml. What was the volume of the water in the beaker?

Before

850 ml

Volume of water | Volume of 6 cubes

After

700 ml

Volume of water | Volume of 4 cubes

Volume of 2 cubes = 850 ml – 700 ml
= 150 ml
Volume of 4 cubes = 2 × 150 ml
= 300 ml
Volume of water in the beaker = 700 ml – 300 ml
= 400 ml

The volume of the water in the beaker was **400 ml**.

Worked Example 2

A tank, measuring 60 cm by 40 cm by 30 cm, was half-filled with water. The water from the tank was poured out to fill 20 identical jars, each of capacity 750 cm^3. What was the height of the water level left in the tank?

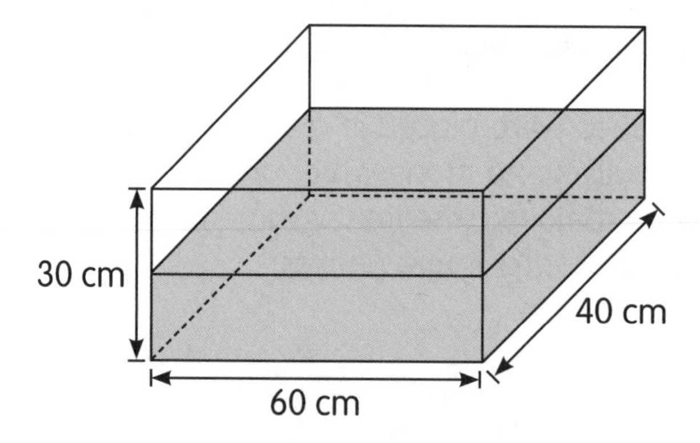

Height of water in the tank = 30 cm ÷ 2
= 15 cm

Volume of water in the tank = 60 cm × 40 cm × 15 cm
= 36,000 cm^3

Total volume of water required to fill 20 jars = 20 × 750 cm^3
= 15,000 cm^3

Volume of water left in the tank = 36,000 cm^3 – 15,000 cm^3
= 21,000 cm^3

Height of the water level left in the tank = $\frac{21{,}000 \text{ cm}^3}{60 \text{ cm} \times 40 \text{ cm}}$
= 8.75 cm

The height of the water level left in the tank was **8.75 cm**.

Answer all questions.

1. A tank, which measures 20 cm by 16 cm by 12 cm, was $\frac{2}{3}$-filled with water. A stone of volume 240 cm^3 was placed into the tank. What was the new height of the water level in the tank?

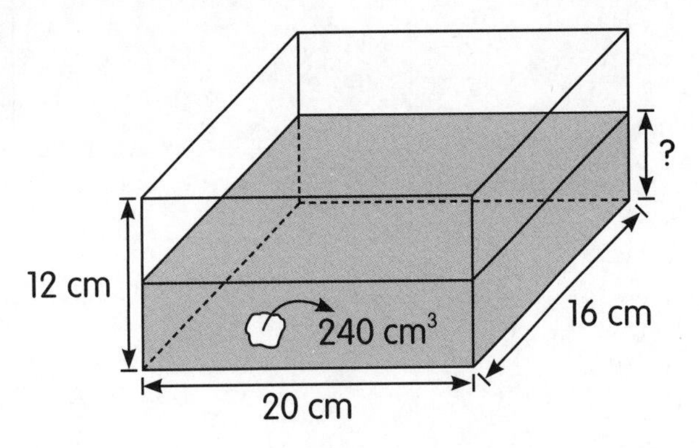

2. The ratio of the volume of water in Container P to the volume of water in Container Q was 5 : 3. When 46 ml of water was poured out from Container P and 120 ml of water was poured into Container Q, both containers had the same volume of water. What was the volume of water in Container P at first?

3. The figure below shows a tank which was $\frac{1}{3}$-filled with water. 50 l of water was added to fill the tank to its brim. What was the height of the water level in the tank at first?

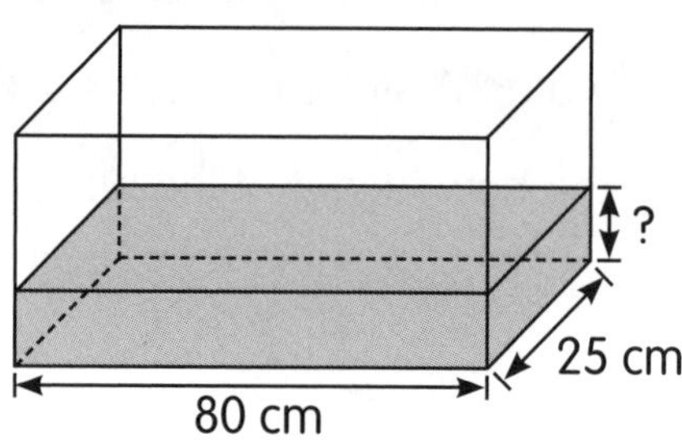

4. The figure below shows $\frac{4}{5}$ of a tank filled with water. After 30 l of water were poured out of the tank, it became $\frac{2}{3}$-full. What was the height of the water level in the tank at first?

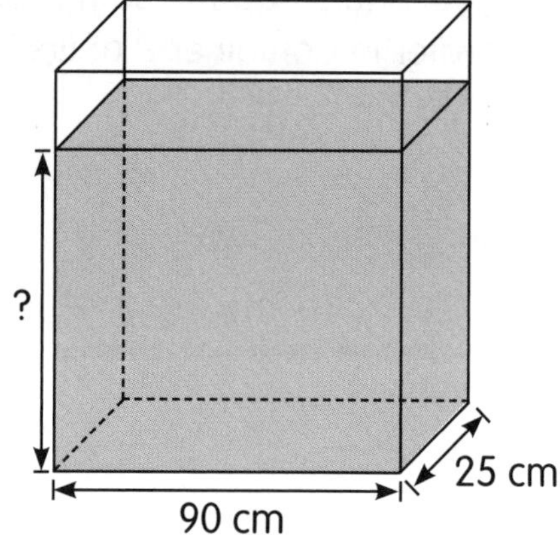

5. A tank, measuring 120 cm by 100 cm by 80 cm, was half filled with water. When 6 identical pails of water were poured into the tank, it became $\frac{4}{5}$-filled. If each pail was filled with water to its brim, what was the capacity of each pail? Give your answer in milliliters.

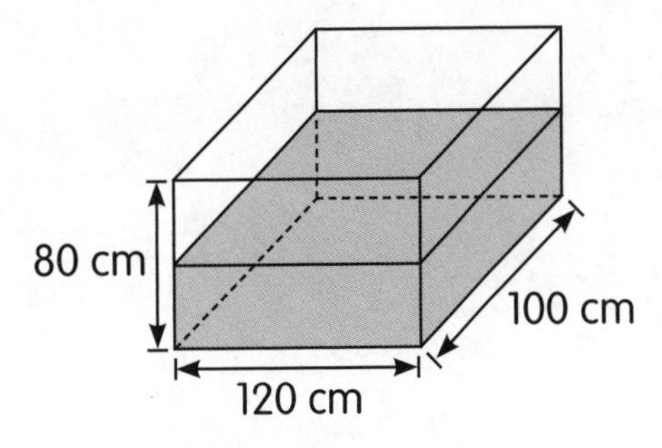

6. A container of capacity 5500 ml contained 2145 ml of water. A 7-cm metal cube was placed in it. How much more water could the container hold? Give your answer in liters and milliliters.

7. A two-liter pitcher contained 764 cm^3 of water. When 12 identical metal cubes were placed into the pitcher, 264 cm^3 of water overflowed. What was the length of each metal cube?

8. Joyce used $\frac{3}{5}$ of the water in a container to fill 4 glasses and 7 cups. If the capacity of each glass was twice that of a cup, how many cups could she fill with the remaining water in the container?

9. Twelve bottles of water can fill $\frac{5}{8}$ of a container. To fill the container completely, another 6 bottles and 5 glasses of water are needed. How many glasses of water have the same capacity as the container?

10. What is the maximum number of rectangular blocks, each measuring 7 cm by 5 cm by 3 cm, that can be placed inside a rectangular box measuring 14 cm by 15 cm by 16 cm?

8 Percentage

Worked Example 1

Jenny and Sylvia have 320 stamps in all. The number of Jenny's stamps is equal to 60% of Sylvia's stamps. How many stamps does Sylvia have?

Sylvia [10 units] } 320
Jenny [6 units]

Sylvia's stamps ⟶ 10 units
Jenny's stamps ⟶ 6 units (60% of 10 units)

16 units ⟶ 320
1 unit ⟶ $320 \div 16 = 20$
10 units ⟶ $10 \times 20 = 200$

Sylvia has **200** stamps.

Worked Example 2

Pearlyn has 10% more stickers than David. If Pearlyn gives 24 stickers to David, David will have 10% more stickers than Pearlyn. How many stickers do Pearlyn and David have in all?

Before

10%

Pearlyn

David

After

24

Pearlyn

David

10%

1 unit ⟶ 24
21 units ⟶ $21 \times 24 = 504$

Pearlyn and David have **504** stickers in all.

Worked Example 3

There are 60 members in a music club. 25% of them like jazz, 15% of them like pop music, 20% of them like rock music, and 50% of the rest like classical music. How many members enjoy classical music?

Percentage of members who like jazz, pop, and rock music
= 25% + 15% + 20%
= 60%

Percentage of members who enjoy other types of music
= 100% – 60%
= 40%

Percentage of members who enjoy classical music
= 50% of 40%
$= \frac{1}{2} \times 40\%$
= 20%

Number of members who enjoy classical music
= 20% of 60
$= \frac{1}{5} \times 60$
= 12

12 members enjoy classical music.

Answer all questions.

1. A total of 48 students sat for a mathematics examination. Only 75% of them passed. How many students passed the examination?

2. During an election, Albert received 60% of the 30 votes cast. Anthony received the remaining votes. How many more votes did Albert receive?

3. A shop owner sold 10 cell phones and made a total profit of 20%. What was his percentage profit for each phone?

4. Samuel bought a watch at a discount of 30%. If he paid $119, what was the original price of the watch?

5. There are some mint chocolates and dark chocolates in a box. The number of mint chocolates is 25% of the number of dark chocolates. What percentage of the chocolates is mint?

6. What is the percentage of the number of whole numbers, from 4 to 23, which are multiples of 5?

7. 50 boys and 30 girls participated in a contest. 20% of the boys and 30% of the girls received prizes. What percentage of the contestants received prizes?

8. Tim wanted to sell his watch at a discount of 10%. However, he then decides to increase the discounted price by 5%. What is the new percentage discount?

9. Serene and Derek have 270 stickers in all. Serene has 25% more stickers than Derek. How many stickers does Derek have?

10. Look at the table below. Find the percentage increase in the number of students who studied French between 2009 and 2010. Give your answer to 2 decimal places.

Year	Number of students who studied French	Total number of students
2009	390	435
2010	420	450

11. There are 120 guests at a birthday party. 30% of them are male. If 25% of the male guests have to leave early, what is the new percentage of male guests left?

Challenging Problems

Worked Example 1

There were 300 books on a shelf. 30% of the books were fiction books and the rest were non-fiction books. When another 120 books were added, the percentage of non-fiction books increased to 75%. How many fiction books were added to the shelf?

Before

Number of fiction books = 30% × 300
= 90

Number of non-fiction books = 70% × 300
= 210

After adding 120 books

Total number of fiction and non-fiction books = 300 + 120
= 420

Number of non-fiction books = 75% × 420
= 315

Number of non-fiction books added = 315 – 210
= 115

Number of fiction books added = 120 – 115
= 5

5 fiction books were added to the shelf.

Worked Example 2

The length of a rectangle is increased by 25%. Its width is decreased by 25%. What is the percentage change in its area?

New length of rectangle = length + 0.25 length
= 1.25 length

New width of rectangle = width – 0.25 width
= 0.75 width

New area in percentage = 1.25 length × 0.75 width × 100%
= 93.75%

Percentage change in area = 100% – 93.75%
= 6.25%

The percentage change in its area is **6.25%**.

Answer all questions.

1. Jonathan sold two television sets for $6000 each. He made a profit of 20% on the first set and made a loss of 20% on the second set. How much profit or loss did he make?

2. If the length and width of a rectangle are increased by 20%, what is the percentage increase in its area?

3. If the length and width of a square are increased by 30%, find the percentage increase in its area.

4. Jack and Jill each had the same amount of money. After six months, Jack's money increased by 10% and Jill's money decreased by 10%. A year later, Jack's money decreased by 10% and Jill's money increased by 10%. Who had more money in the end?

5. At a fruits stall, 30% of the fruits are oranges, 40% are apples, and the rest are pineapples. If 20% of the oranges and 30% of the apples are rotten, what percentage of the fruits are in good condition?

6. Melvin has 30% more marbles than Henry. If Melvin gives 30 marbles to Henry, both of them will have the same number of marbles. How many marbles does Henry have?

7. Bobby takes 66 candies from a jar and Mike takes the remaining candies. If Bobby gives 24 candies to Mike, the number of candies Mike has will increase by 60%. How many candies must Bobby give to Mike so that they will have the same number of candies?

8. Dave had 400 old Singapore and Malaysia coins. 60% of the coins were Singapore coins. After buying more Singapore coins, the percentage of Malaysia coins decreased by 8%. How many Singapore coins did he buy?

9. There were 400 stamps in the album. 35% of them were Indonesia stamps and the rest were Malaysia stamps. When 100 more stamps were added, the percentage of Malaysia stamps increased to 70%. How many Indonesia stamps were added to the album?

10. If 25% of Number A is 125 and 0.35% of Number B is 10.5, what is the sum of numbers A and B?

9 Angles and Triangles

Worked Example 1

In the figure below, the value of $\angle x$ is twice the value of $\angle y$. Find $\angle x$ and $\angle y$.

120°

x

y

Since the sum of angles at a point is 360°,

$$\angle x + \angle y + 90° + 120° = 360°$$
$$\angle x + \angle y = 360° - 90° - 120°$$
$$= 150°$$

Since $\angle x = 2\ \angle y$,

$$2\ \angle y + \angle y = 150°$$
$$3\ \angle y = 150°$$
$$\angle y = 150° \div 3$$
$$= 50°$$

$$\angle x = 2 \times 50°$$
$$= 100°$$

Hence, $\angle x$ = **100°** and $\angle y$ = **50°**.

Worked Example 2

In the figure below, AB and CD are straight lines. Find ∠AOC, ∠AOD and ∠BOC.

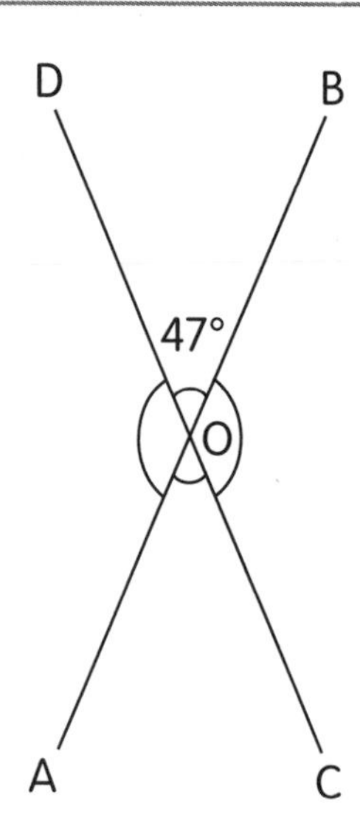

Since ∠AOC and ∠BOD are vertically opposite angles,
∠AOC = 47°

Since ∠AOD and ∠BOD are angles on a straight line,
∠AOD = 180° – 47°
= 133°

Since ∠AOD and ∠BOC are vertically opposite angles,
∠BOC = 133°

Hence, ∠AOC = **47°**, ∠AOD = **133°**, and ∠BOC = **133°**.

Worked Example 3

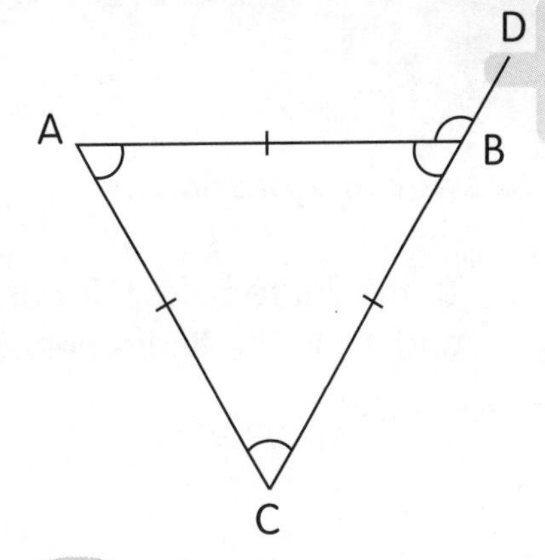

An equilateral triangle has 3 equal angles. Each angle is 60°.
Hence, $\angle A = \angle B = \angle C = 60°$.

$\angle ABD = 180° - 60°$
$= 120°$

Hence, $\angle ABD =$ **120°**.

Worked Example 4

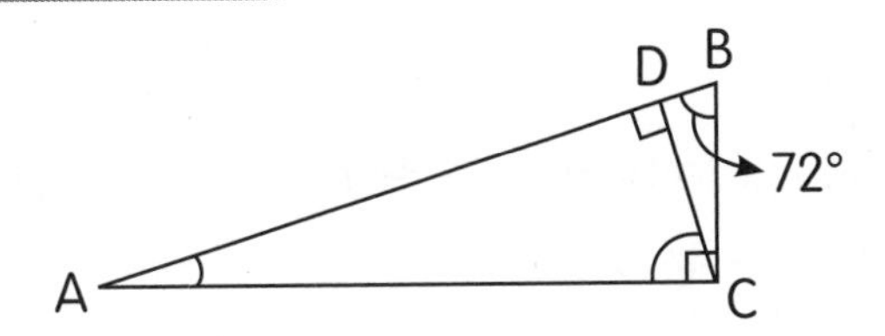

$\angle BAC = 180° - 90° - 72°$
$= 18°$

$\angle DCA = 180° - 18° - 90°$
$= 72°$

Hence, $\angle BAC =$ **18**° and $\angle DCA =$ **72**°.

Practice Questions

Answer all questions.

1. In the figure below, PQ and RS are straight lines. Find the value of $\angle x$ and $\angle y$ in the figure below.

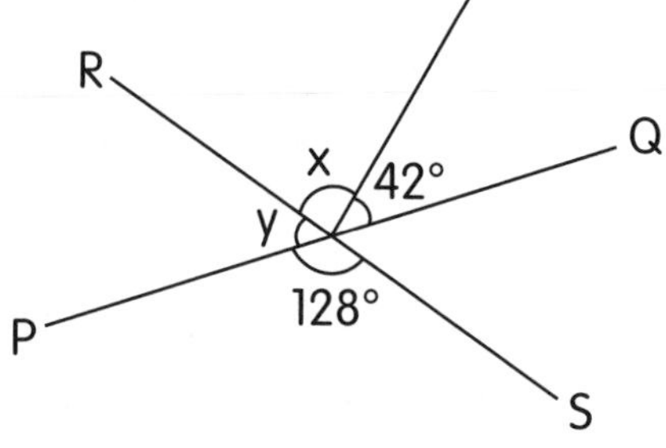

2. In the figure below, find $\angle x$.

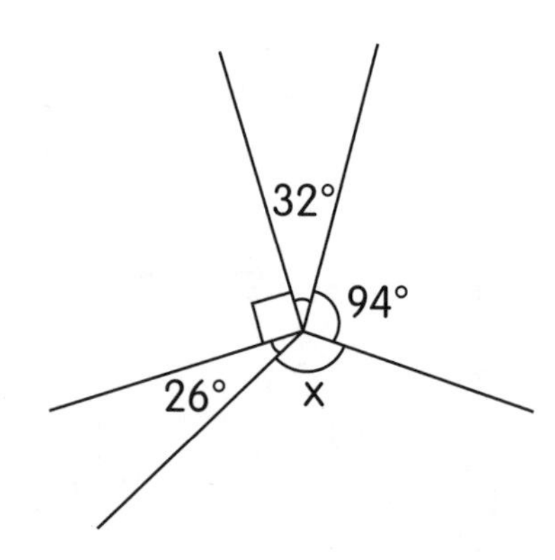

3 . In the figure below, RS, PQ and TU are straight lines. Find $\angle x$.

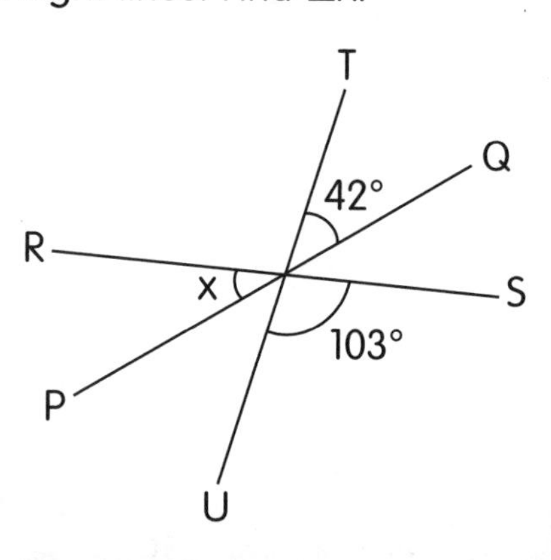

4. In the figure below, XY is a straight line. What is the value of $\angle z$?

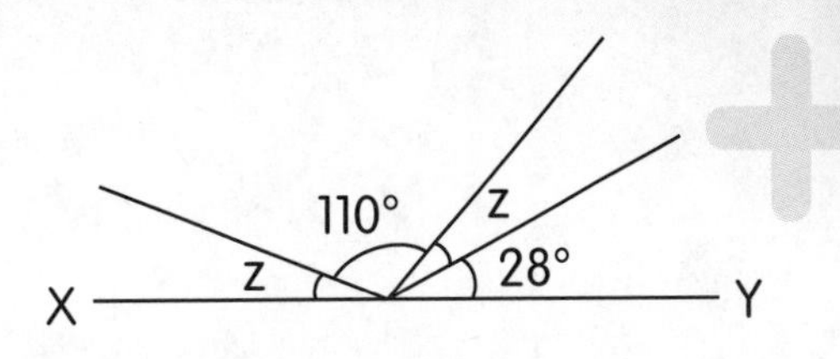

5. In the figure below, what is the value of $\angle q$?

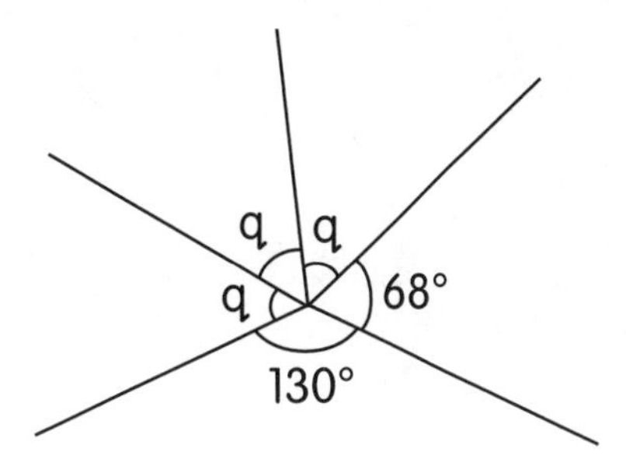

6. In the figure below, the value of $\angle x$ is five times the value of $\angle y$. What is the value of $\angle x$ and $\angle y$?

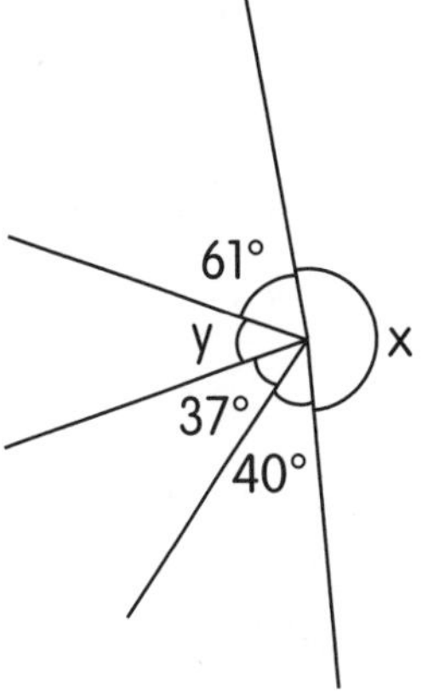

7. In triangle PQR, PQ = RQ and ∠RQP = 76°. Find ∠QPR and ∠PRQ.

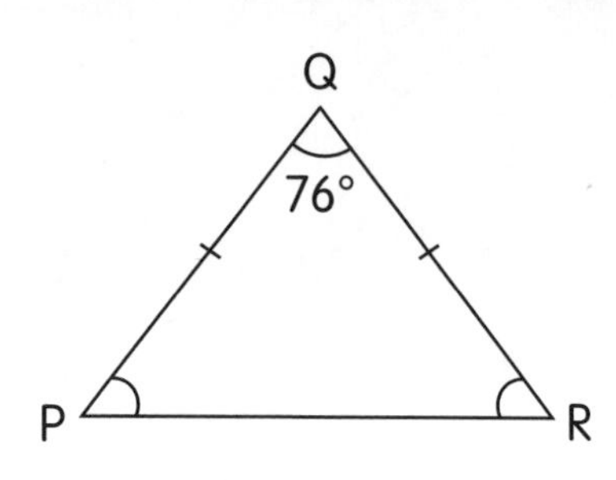

8. In the figure below, ABC is an equilateral triangle and AE = AD.
Find ∠ADE.

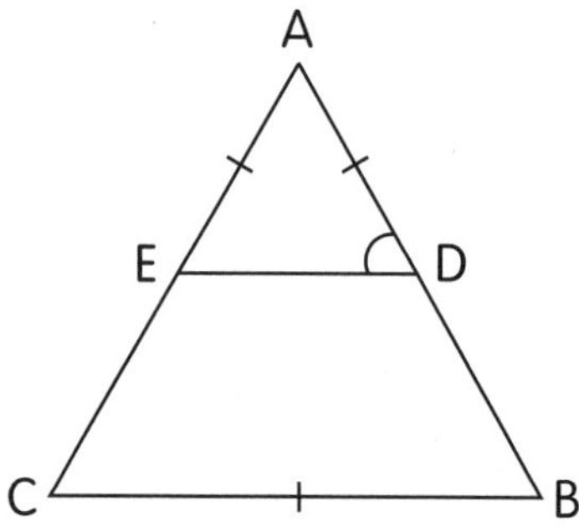

9. In triangle PQR, PR = QR. Find ∠PQS.

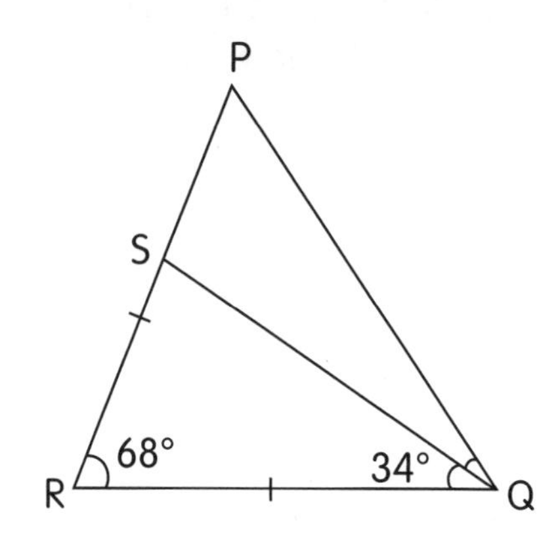

10. In the figure below, AB is a straight line. Find ∠p.

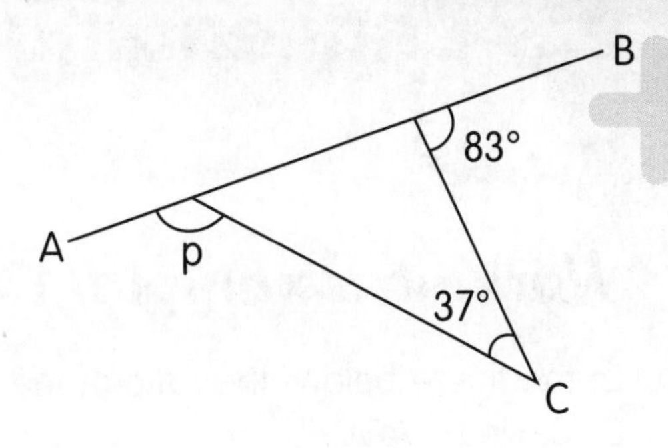

11. Triangle ABC is an isosceles triangle and CA = CB. Find ∠x.

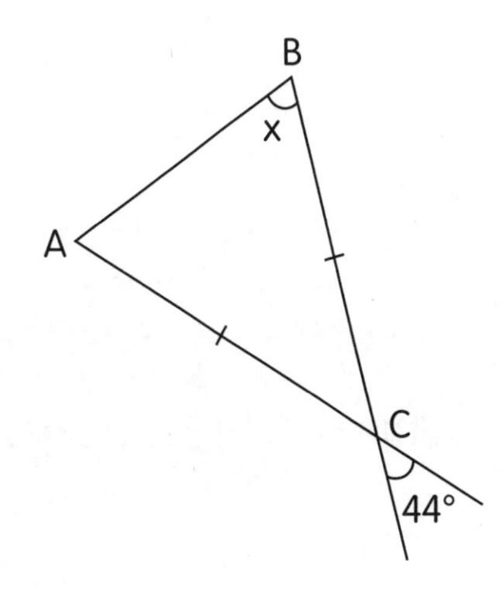

Challenging Problems

Worked Example 1

In the figure below, the ratio of the value of ∠AOB to the value of ∠AOD is 2 : 3. Find ∠AOD.

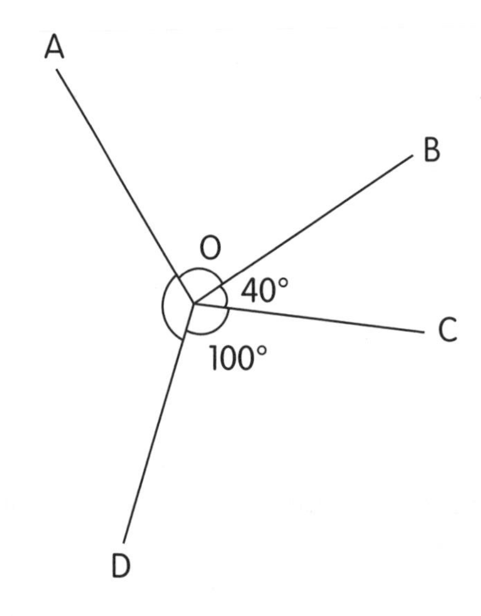

5 units ⟶ 360° – 100° – 40° = 220°
1 unit ⟶ 220° ÷ 5 = 44°
3 units ⟶ 3 × 44° = 132°

The value of ∠AOD is **132°**.

Answer all questions.

1. In the figure below, the ratio of the value of $\angle POQ$ to the value of $\angle POS$ is 5 : 3. Find $\angle POQ$.

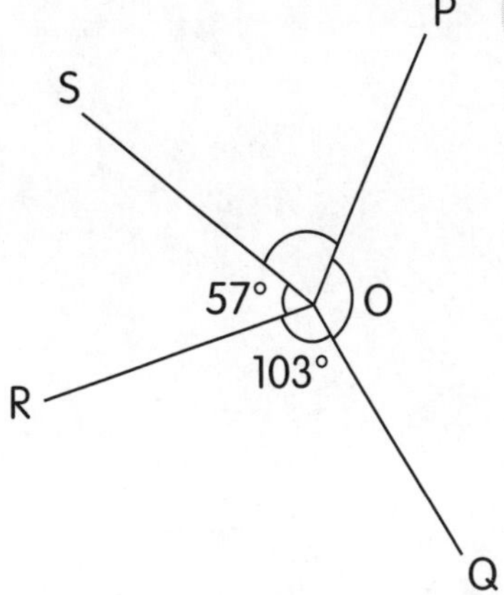

2. In the figure below, AD and BE are straight lines. Find $\angle p$ and $\angle q$.

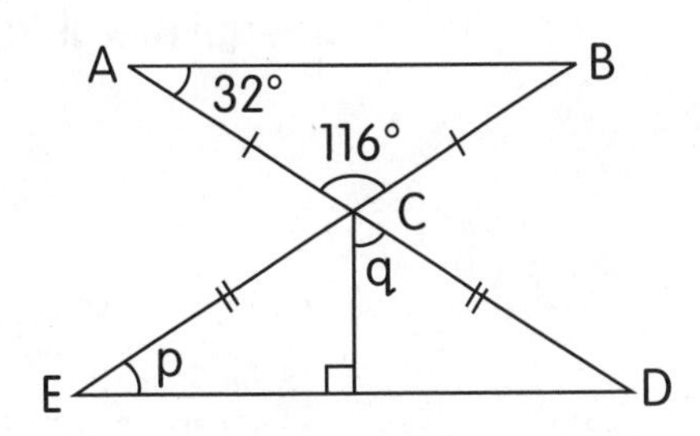

3. In the figure below, PRT and PQT are isosceles triangles. If RQ is a straight line, find ∠a and ∠b.

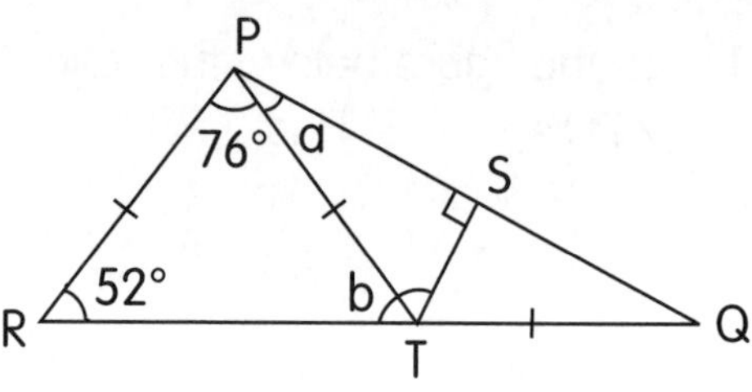

4. In the figure below, QT is a straight line, PRQ is a right-angled triangle and STR is an equilateral triangle. Find ∠z.

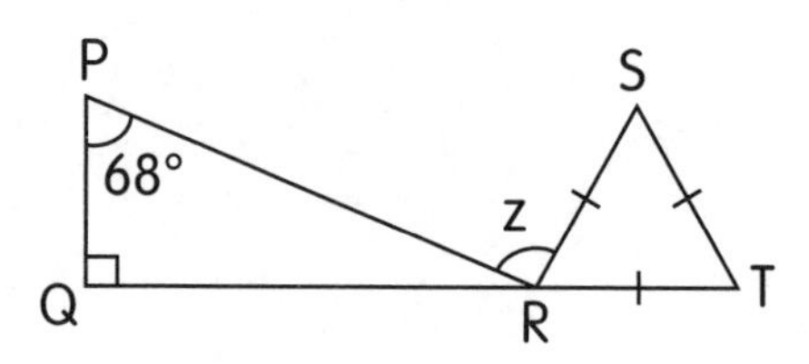

5. In the figure below, PQRS is a square. Find $\angle a$.

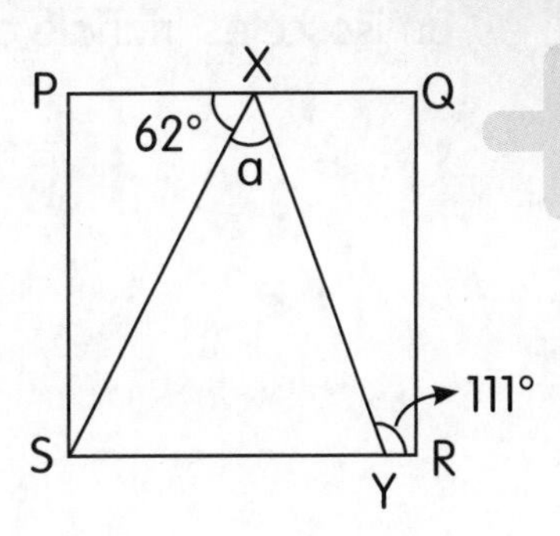

6. In the figure below, PAY is an isosceles triangle and AB is a straight line. Find $\angle YAP$.

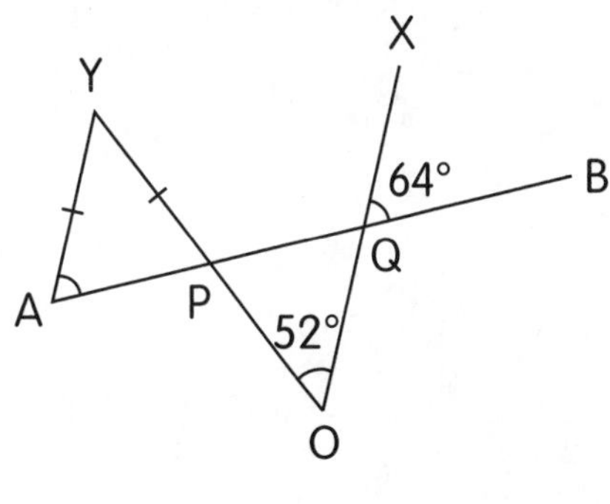

7. The figure is made up of two triangles XYZ and XVW. If triangle XYZ is an isosceles triangle and XY = XZ, find ∠p.

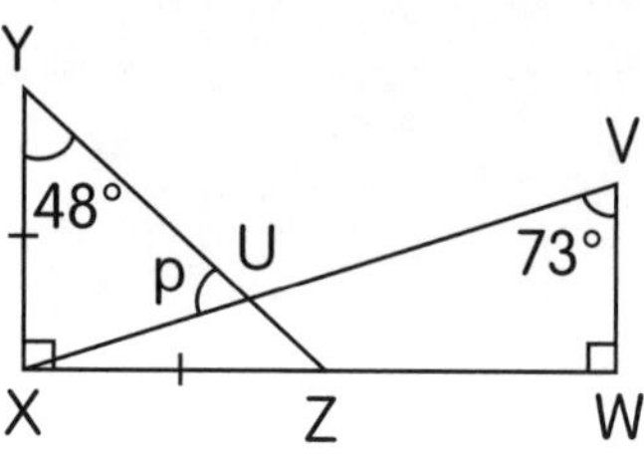

8. Triangle PQR is an isosceles triangle. Triangle QSR is an equilateral triangle. Find ∠y.

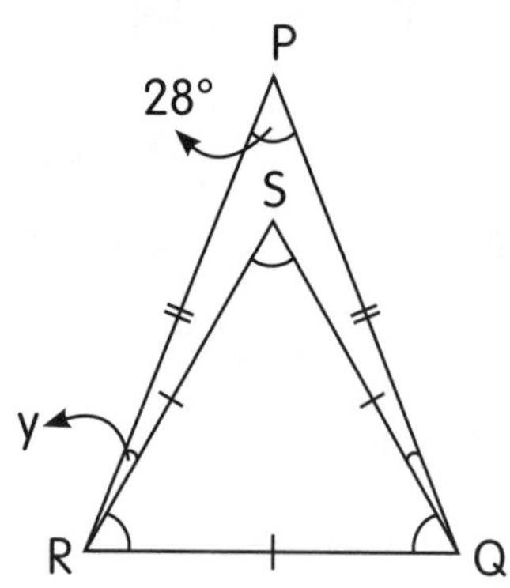

9. The figure is made up of two triangles, PQT and PST. $\angle PTR = 17°$ and $\angle RPQ = 32°$. If triangle PST is an isosceles triangle, find $\angle y$.

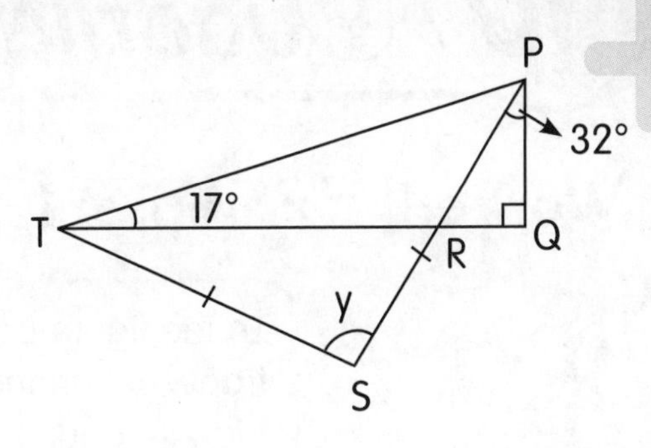

10. What is the sum of the six unknown marked angles?

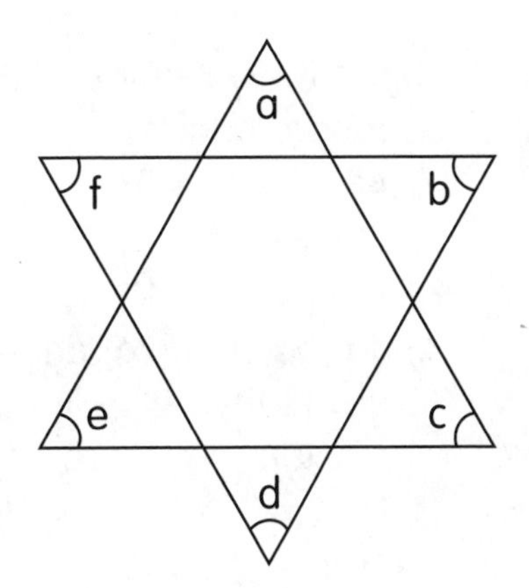

Worked Example 1

In the figure below, ABCD is a trapezoid, triangle ADE is an isosceles triangle and ED = EA. Find ∠x.

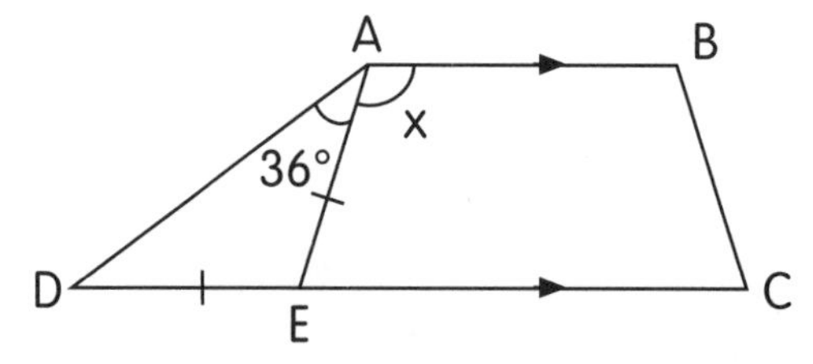

Since triangle ADE is an isosceles triangle,
∠EAD = ∠EDA = 36°

Since the exterior angle of a triangle is equal to the sum of the interior opposite angles,
∠AEC = 36° + 36°
= 72°

Since each pair of angles between two parallel sides add up to 180°,
∠x = 180° − 72°
= 108°

Hence, ∠x = **108°**.

Worked Example 2

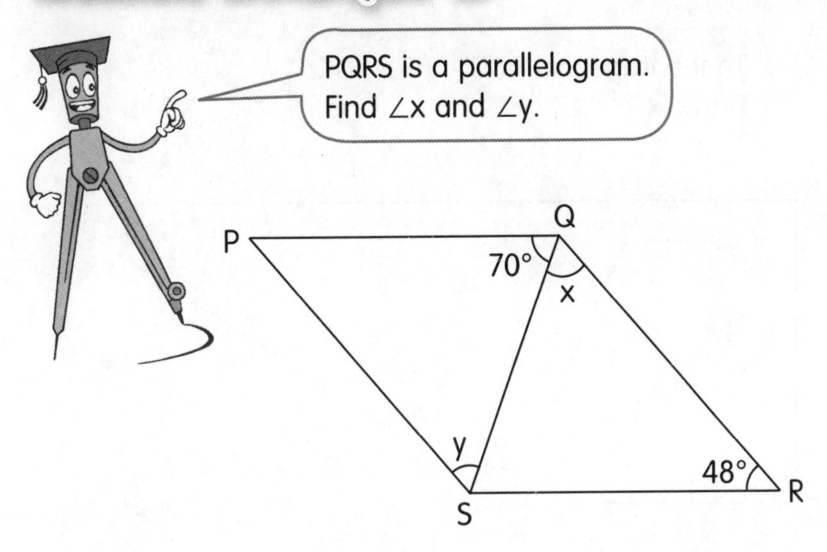

Since each pair of angles between two parallel sides add up to 180°,

$\angle x + 48° + 70° = 180°$

$\angle x = 180° - 70° - 48°$

$= 62°$

Since the opposite angles of a parallelogram are equal, $\angle SPQ = 48°$.

$\angle y = 180° - \angle PQS - \angle SPQ$

$= 180° - 70° - 48°$

$= 62°$

Hence, $\angle x =$ **62°** and $\angle y =$ **62°**.

Worked Example 3

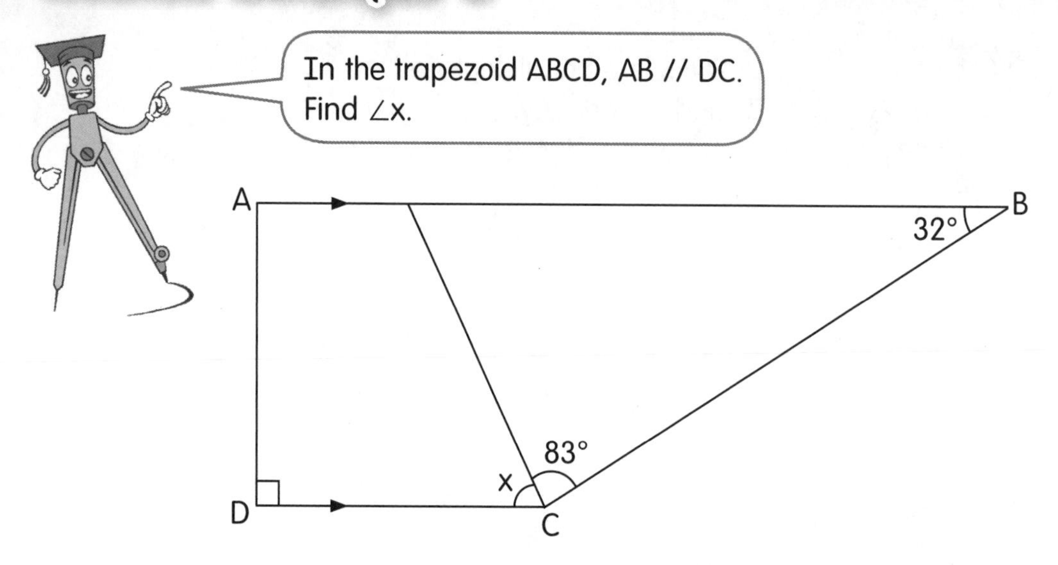

Since each pair of angles between two parallel lines adds up to 180°, ∠ABC + ∠BCD = 180°.

$\angle BCD = 180° - 32°$
$= 148°$

$\angle x + 83° = 148°$
$\angle x = 148° - 83°$
$= 65°$

Hence, ∠x = **65°**.

Answer all questions.

1. In the figure below, ABCD is a parallelogram. Find ∠p.

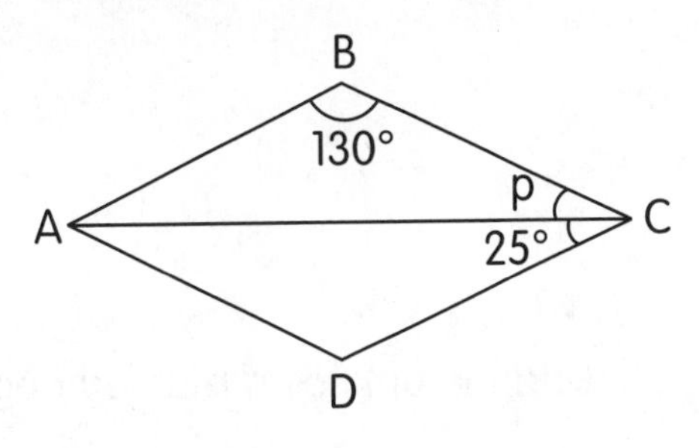

2. In the figure below, ABCD is a parallelogram. Find ∠CBD.

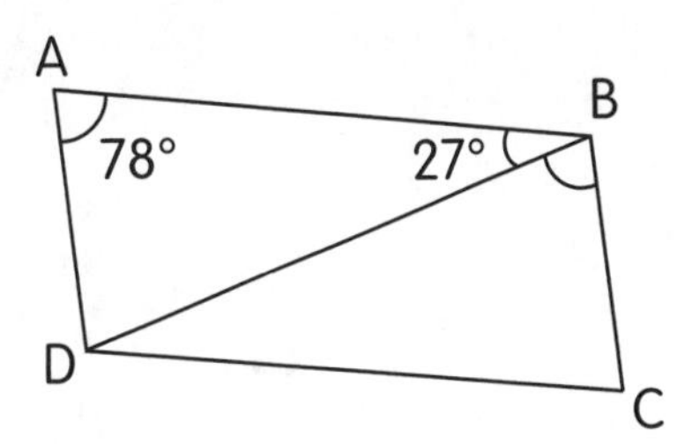

3. In the figure below, PQRS is a parallelogram. Find ∠y.

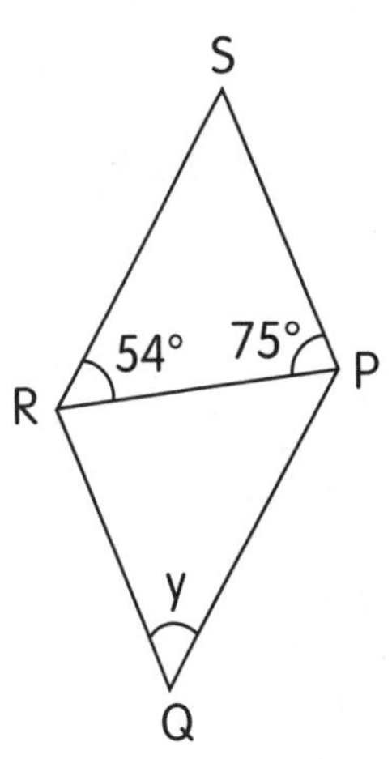

4. In the figure below, PQRS is a parallelogram. Find ∠SQR.

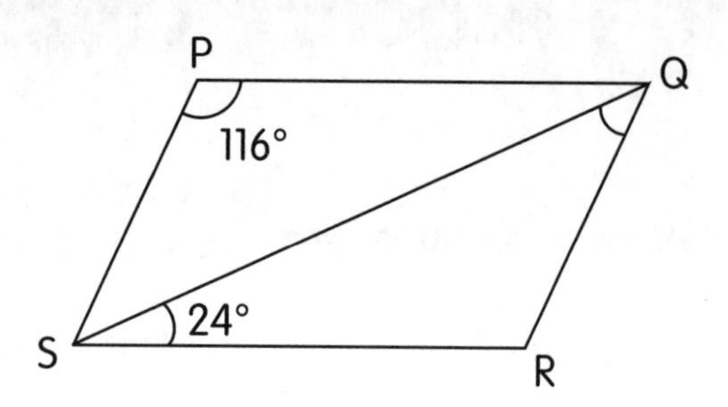

5. Find the unknown marked angles in the parallelogram ABCD.

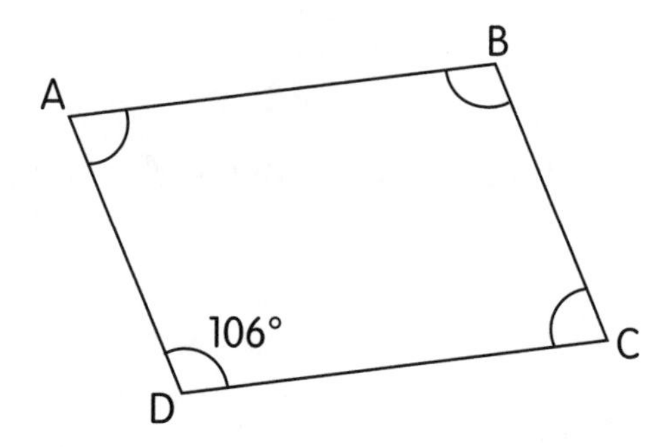

6. Find the unknown marked angles in the rhombus ABCD.

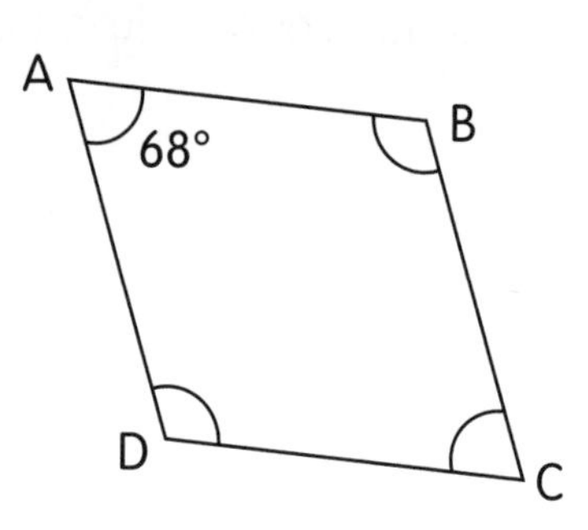

7. In the figure below, EFGH is a rhombus. Find ∠x.

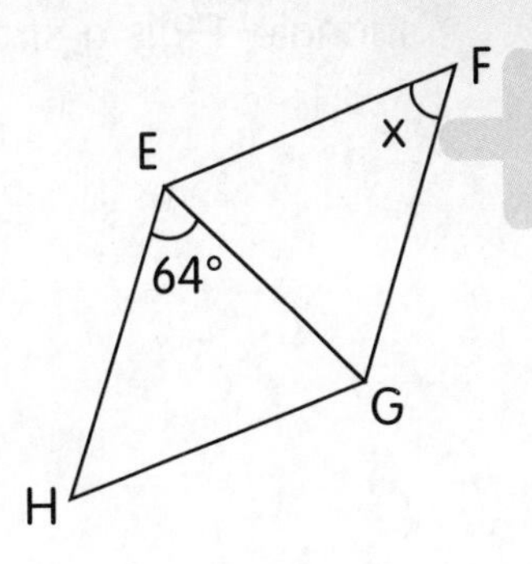

8. In trapezoid PQRS, PQ // SR. Find ∠PST.

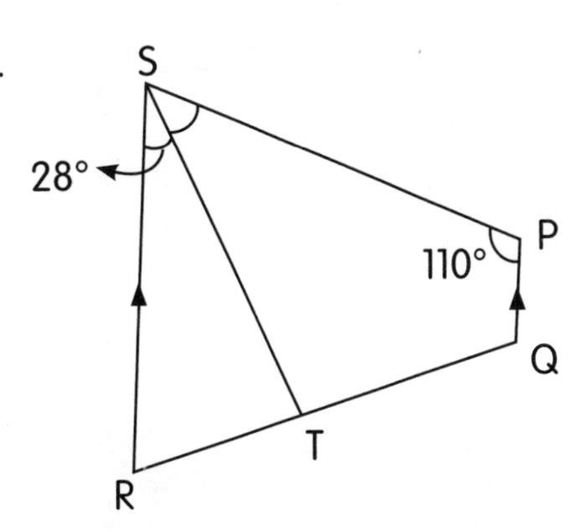

9. In the figure below, PQST is a parallelogram, QRS is an isosceles triangle, PR is a straight line and RQ = RS. Find ∠x and ∠y.

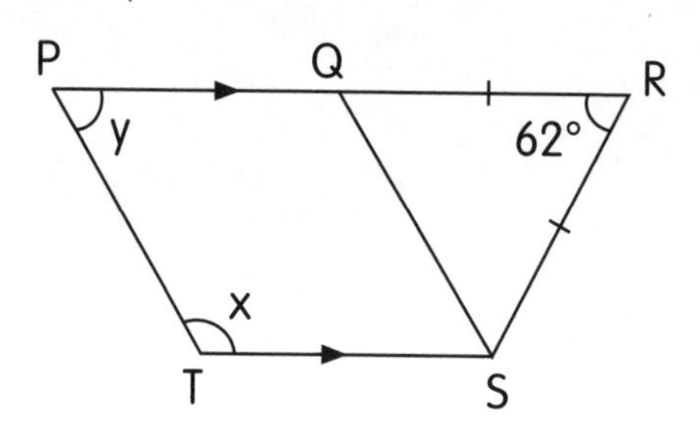

10. In trapezoid ABCD, AB // DC, ADE is an isosceles triangle and EA = ED. Find ∠ADC.

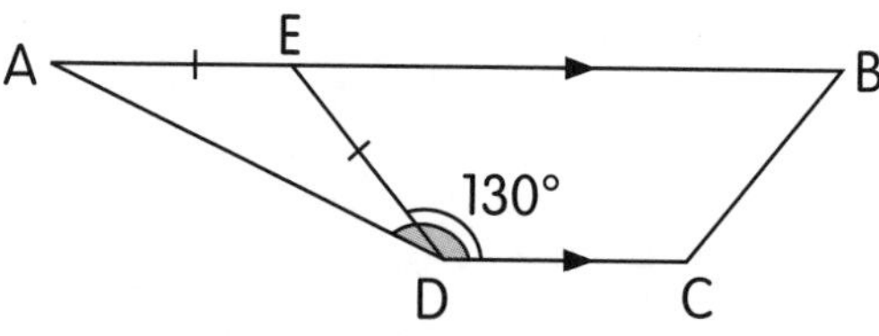

Worked Example 1

In square ABCD, DBE is a straight line and AE = CE. If ∠AEC = 70°, find ∠x.

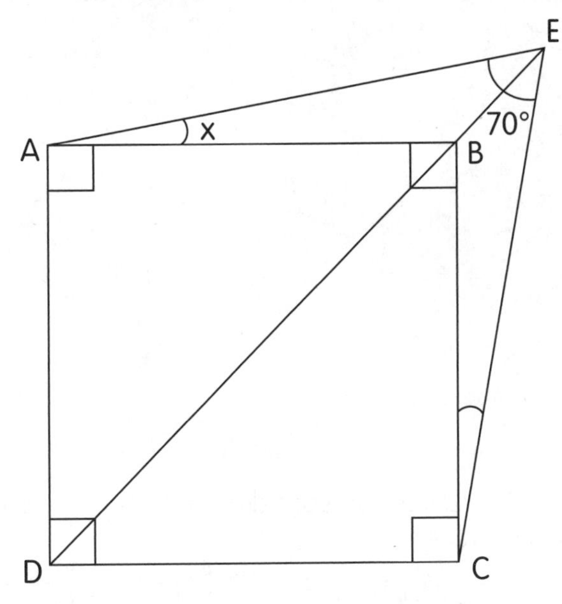

Since AE = CE, A and C are the vertices of the square ABCD, triangle ACE is an isosceles triangle.

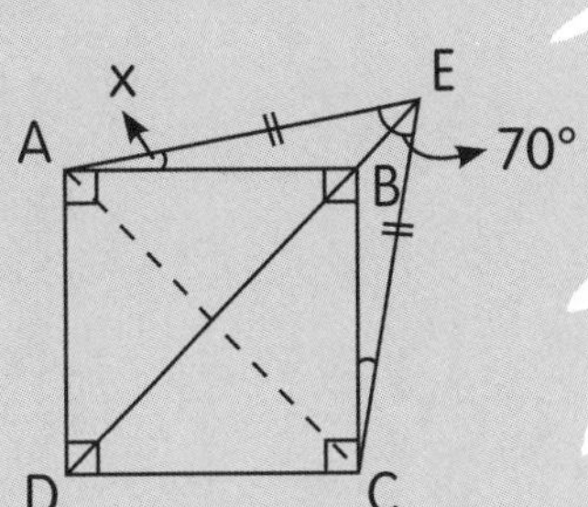

∠AEC = 70°

∠CAE = ∠ECA
= (180° – 70°) ÷ 2
= 55°

Since CA is the diagonal of square ABDC,
∠CAB = 45°

∠x = 55° – 45°
= 10°

Hence, ∠x = **10°**.

Answer all questions.

1. In the figure below, EFGI is a trapezoid, EFHI is a parallelogram and FGH is an isosceles triangle where HG = HF. Find ∠FGH.

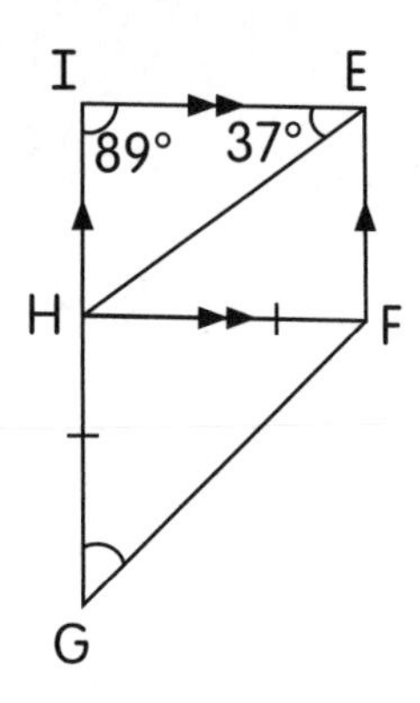

2. In rectangle KLMN, PLM is an isosceles triangle, LP = LM and ∠KNP = 28°. Find ∠NPM.

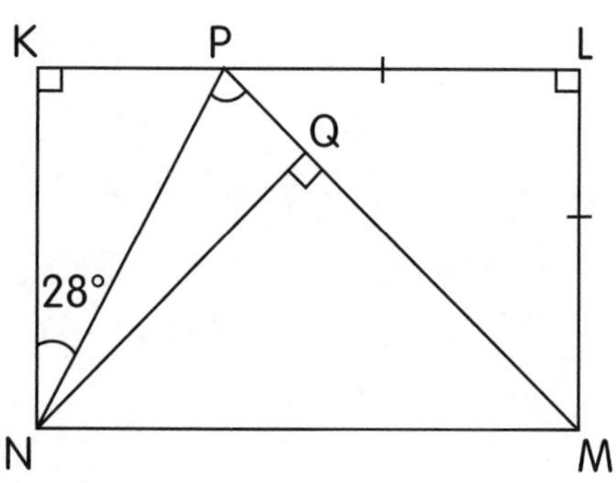

3. In the figure below, PQR is an isosceles triangle, where RP = RQ and PQRS is a trapezoid. Find ∠SRQ.

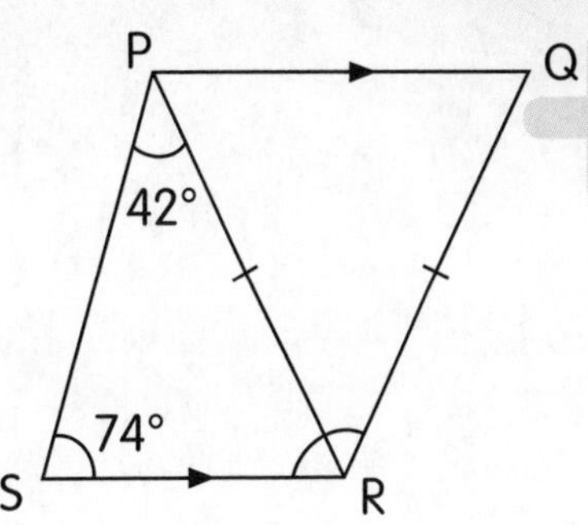

4. In the figure below, ABCE is a rectangle. Find ∠EBD.

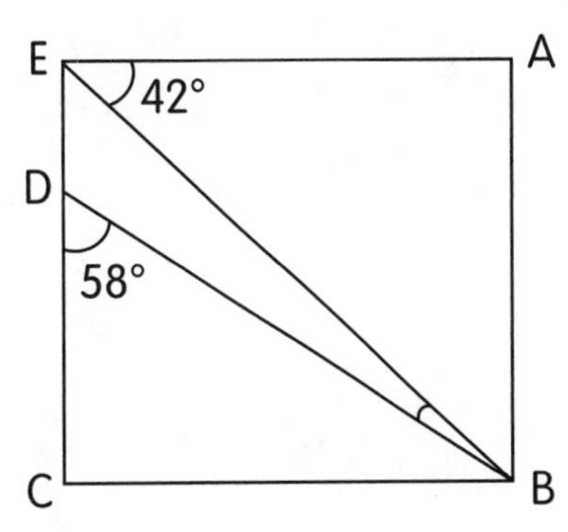

5. PQRS and QRTU are parallelograms. Find ∠PQS.

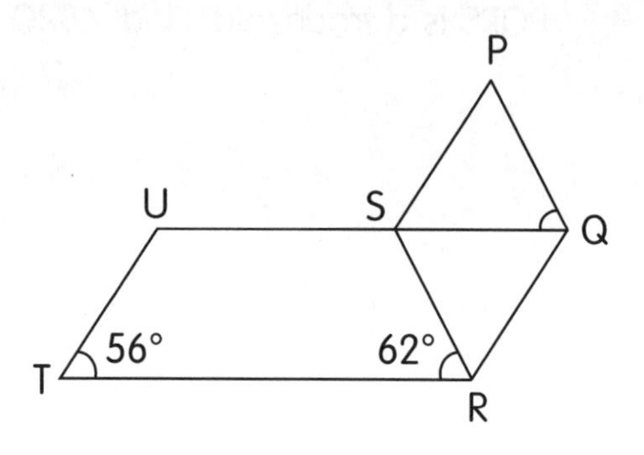

6. In rectangle PQRS, ADB is a straight line, SA = SB and BRC is an equilateral triangle. Find ∠ABC.

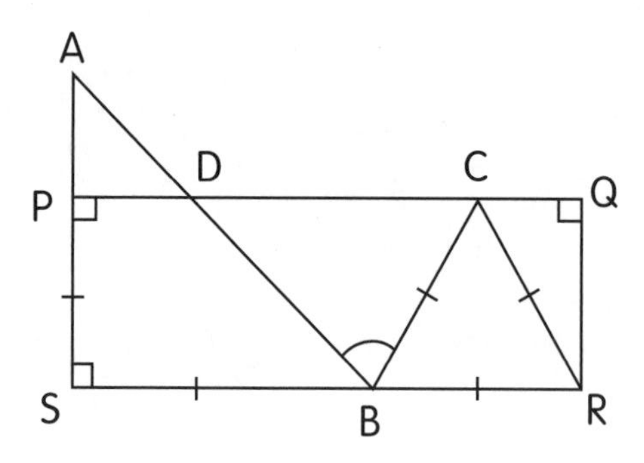

7. In trapezoid PQRS, PQ // SR, PR and SQ are straight lines. If PQ = PS, find ∠QTR.

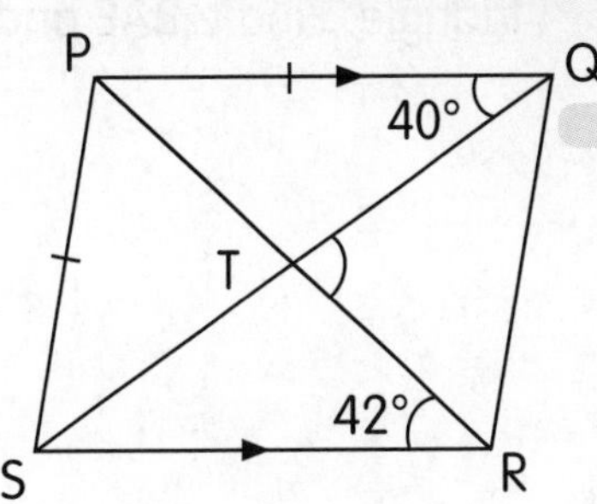

8. In the figure below, PQRS is a parallelogram and ABCD is a rectangle. If ∠APB = 105° and ∠DCR = 38°, find ∠CBQ.

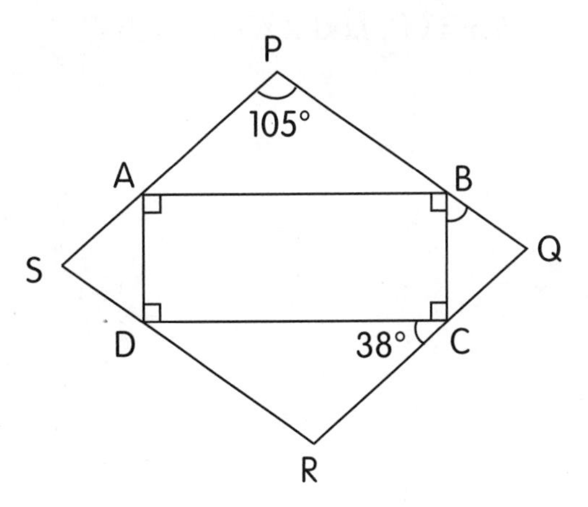

9. In the figure below, ABCD is a parallelogram and BCE is an isosceles triangle. Find ∠BAE and ∠BEA.

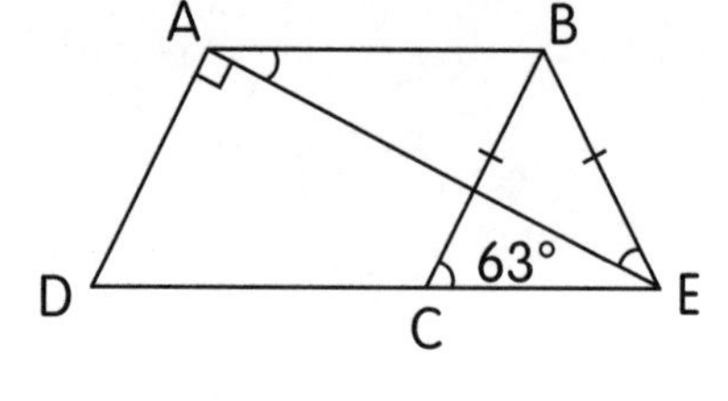

10. In the figure below, ABCD is a square and BEC is an equilateral triangle. If ABE and CDE are isosceles triangles, where BA = BE and CE = CD, find ∠x.

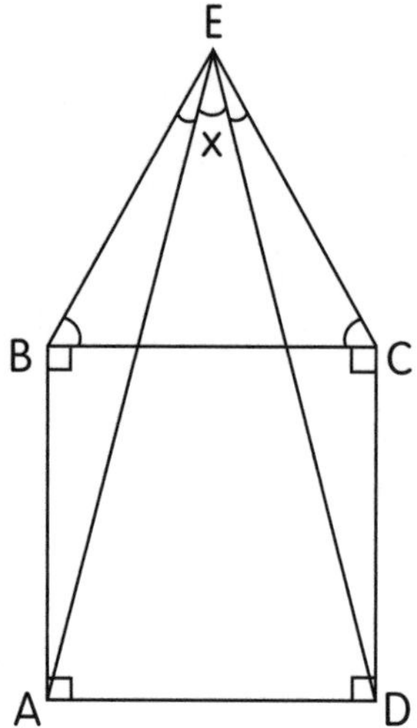

11 Average

Worked Example 1

The average income of Adam, Irene, and Fiona is \$560. Irene earns twice as much as Adam. Fiona earns twice as much as Irene. How much does Fiona earn?

Adam
Irene
Fiona
3 × \$560

7 units ⟶ 3 × \$560 = \$1680
1 unit ⟶ \$1680 ÷ 7 = \$240
4 units ⟶ 4 × \$240 = \$960

Fiona earns **\$960**.

Worked Example 2

The average of six numbers is 6. If 3 is subtracted from four of the numbers, what is the new average?

Since the average of six numbers is 6, then the total sum of the six numbers is $6 \times 6 = 36$.

If 3 is subtracted from four of the numbers, we subtract $4 \times 3 = 12$ from the sum.

New sum $= 36 - 12$
$\quad = 24$

New average $= 24 \div 6$
$\quad = 4$

The new average is **4**.

Answer all questions.

1. The digits 2, 3, and 7 can form six different 3-digit numbers. Find the average of these six numbers.

2. Lynette's average score for five tests is 18. If she scores 24 points for her sixth test, what is her average score for all six tests?

3. Robin received an average score of 64 points for his first three tests. In his fourth test, he scored 28 points more than the average score for his first three tests. What is his new average score?

4. The average of five numbers is 7. If one of the five numbers is removed, the average of the four remaining numbers is 6. What is the value of the number that was removed?

5. The average test score of Sean and Ted is 68 points. The average test score of Sean, Ted and Mary is 72 points. What is Mary's test score?

6. In a test, the average score of 25 boys and 15 girls is 68 points. The average score of the boys is 62 points. What is the average score of the girls?

7. There are 100 black paper clips, 150 white paper clips, and 250 silver paper clips in a box. The average weight of the paper clips is 3.9 g.
   (a) Find the total weight of the paper clips.
   (b) If the box of paper clips weighs 2596 g, what is the weight of the empty box?

8. Eugene's average score of three tests is 85 points. If he wants his average score to increase by 2 points, what score must he get for the fourth test?

9. The total weight of eight tennis players is 645 kg and the average weight of seven baseball players is 90 kg. What is the average weight of all the players?

10. Bill read 61 pages of a book on the first day, 49 pages on the second day, and 52 pages on the third day. On the fourth day, he read 6 pages more than the average number of pages he had read on the first three days. How many pages did he read on the fourth day?

Challenging Problems

Worked Example 1

In a Mathematics test, a class of 21 students scored an average of 97 points. The maximum possible score of the test is 100 points. What is the least possible score that any of the 21 students could have scored?

Total points scored = 21 × 97
= 2037

If all but one student had scored the maximum possible score, then the remaining student would have scored the least possible score.

Least possible points scored = 2037 – (20 × 100)
= 37

The least possible score that any of the 21 students could have obtained is **37**.

Worked Example 2

Find the average of the 100 whole numbers from 1 to 100.

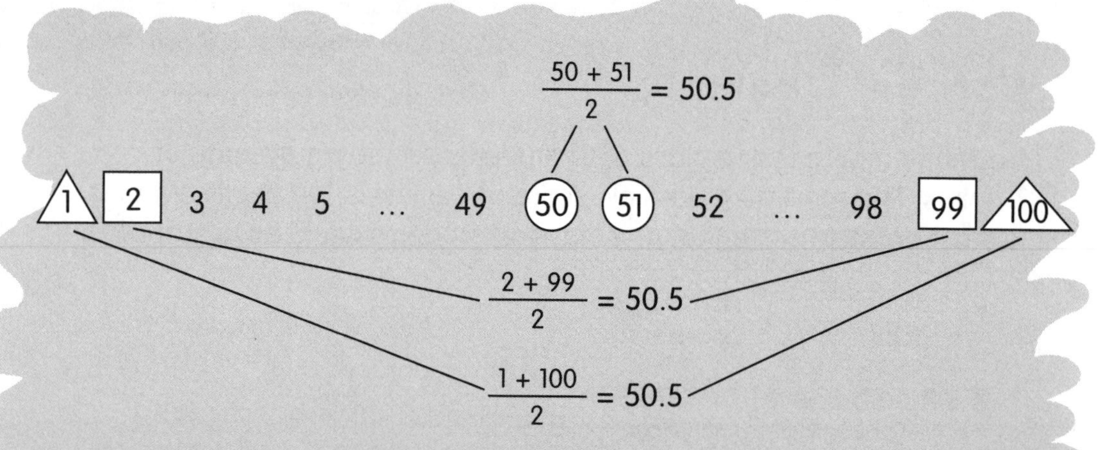

The average of each pair of numbers is 50.5.

Hence, the average of the 100 whole numbers from 1 to 100 is **50.5**.

Answer all questions.

1. Maria scored an average of 90 points for six tests. The total score of each test is 100 points. Find the lowest possible score she could have obtained.

2. Find the average of the 1000 whole numbers from 1 to 1000.

3. Twelve cinemas have an average of 800 customers each day. If four of the cinemas close down, but the total number of customers remains the same, what is the new average number of customers?

4. The average height of Esther, Felicia, and George is 151 cm. Esther is 8 cm shorter than Felicia, and George is 19 cm taller than Esther. Find the height of Esther, Felicia, and George.

5. There are 5 packages in a room. If each package has a different weight, and the average weight of the packages is 16 kg, what is the heaviest that a package could be?

6. The average weight of a group of adults is 72 kg. $\frac{4}{9}$ of the adults are men, and the rest are women. The average weight of the men is 82 kg. What is the average weight of the women?

7. The average of 16 consecutive odd numbers is 122. Find the smallest odd number.

8. The average of 10 consecutive odd numbers is 100. Find the sum of the smallest and greatest odd number.

9. The average test scores of Aaron and Bob is 16. The average test scores of Bob and Chris is 18. The average test score of Chris and Dawn is 21. What is the average test score of Aaron and Dawn?

10. Tyler needs to score 100 points for his final Mathematics test of the year to improve his average score from 76 to 79. How many Mathematics tests are there in the year?

12 Rate

Worked Example 1

The table below shows the rates of charges for a golf club membership. Roger wants to join the golf club for one and a half years. How much does he need to pay?

One-time application fee	$1450
Monthly membership fee	$85

$1\frac{1}{2}$ years ⟶ 18 months

Membership fee for 18 months = 18 × $85
= $1530

Total amount of money = $1450 + $1530
= $2980

He needs to pay **$2980**.

Worked Example 2

Six men can pack 1500 boxes in 4 days. At the same rate, how many boxes can eight men pack in 6 days?

Method 1

Number of boxes 6 men can pack in 4 days ⟶ 1500

Number of boxes 8 men can pack in 4 days ⟶ $\frac{1500}{6} \times 8 = 2000$

Number of boxes 8 men can pack in 6 days ⟶ $\frac{2000}{4} \times 6 = 3000$

Eight men can pack **3000** boxes in 6 days.

Method 2

Number of boxes 6 men can pack in 4 days ⟶ 1500

Number of boxes 6 men can pack in 6 days ⟶ $\frac{1500}{4} \times 6 = 2250$

Number of boxes 8 men can pack in 6 days ⟶ $\frac{2250}{6} \times 8 = 3000$

Eight men can pack **3000** boxes in 6 days.

Practice Questions

Answer all questions.

1. The table below shows the rates of charges at a parking lot.

For the first hour or part thereof	$2.80
For every subsequent half an hour or part thereof	$2.20

   Glenn parked his car in the parking lot from 9:10 a.m. to 10:50 a.m.
   How much did he have to pay?

2. Water flowing from a tap can fill a tub in 10 min. At this rate, how long does it take to fill the same tub from two similar taps?

3. A photocopier can staple 360 booklets in 15 min.
   (a) How many booklets can the photocopier staple in 20 min?
   (b) How long would the photocopier take to staple 600 booklets?

4. Fifty students have to pay $30 each to charter a bus. If there are only 40 students and the cost to charter a bus remains the same, how much will each student need to pay?

5. Ann takes 8 min to run round the school track. Sophie can run round the school track eight times in 1 h. Who is faster?

6. A machine produces 53 loaves of bread per hour. If the machine operates 24 h a day, how many loaves of bread can the machine produce in 5 days?

7. The rent for 10 machines is $400 per month. The rent for 15 machines is $550 per month. At this rate, what is the rent for 25 machines?

8. A snail crawls along a ruler from the 16-cm mark to the 10-cm mark in 5 s. At this rate, how long will it take to reach the 1-cm mark?

9. Ten workers can dig 20 holes in 40 days. At the same rate, how many days would 20 workers take to dig 10 holes?

10. Three clerks can type six documents in 12 days. At this rate, how long will it take for two clerks to type three such documents?

Worked Example 1

Two pipes are used to fill a pool with water. Water flowing from the first pipe can fill the pool in 3 h. Water flowing from the second pipe can fill the pool in 4 h. If water is flowing out from both pipes, how long will it take to fill the pool?

In 1 h, water flowing from the first pipe can fill $\frac{1}{3}$ of the pool.

In 1 h, water flowing from the second pipe can fill $\frac{1}{4}$ of the pool.

In 1 h, water flowing from both pipes can fill $\frac{1}{3} + \frac{1}{4} = \frac{7}{12}$ of the pool.

Time taken to fill the pool with water $\longrightarrow 1 \div \frac{7}{12} = 1\frac{5}{7}$ h

It will take $\mathbf{1\frac{5}{7}}$ **h** to fill the pool with water.

Answer all questions.

1. Clock A gains 5 min every hour and Clock B gains 8 min every hour. At noon, the minute hands of both clocks point at 12 at the same time. How many hours later will the minute hands of both clocks point at the same time again?

2. Tap A fills a tub with cold water in 6 min. Tap B fills the same tub with hot water in 8 min. If water is flowing out from taps A and B at the same time, how long does it take to fill the tub?

3. The cost for five guests to stay at a hotel for 7 days is $2275. At this rate, how much will it cost three guests to stay at the same hotel for 4 days?

4. The table below shows the rates of charges for taxi fare in a city.

For the first two km	$2.80
For every subsequent 300 meters or part thereof	$0.30

If Clare traveled a distance of 19.8 km, how much did she pay for the taxi fare?

5. In a hostel, there are 120 kg of rice for 80 students to consume for 12 days. Each student is given the same amount of rice everyday.
   (a) If 16 new students join the hostel, how many days will the students take to consume 120 kg of rice?
   (b) If the hostel receives a donation of 40 kg of rice, how many days more will the 80 students take to consume them?

6. Three men take 2 days to paint 5 fences. At this rate, how many days will it take for two men to paint 1 fence?

7. Six men can pack 900 boxes in 4 days. At this rate, how many boxes can ten men pack in 6 days?

8. Aileen takes 2 days and Eve takes 3 days to sew 48 dresses altogether. If Aileen takes 4 days and Eve takes 2 days to sew 64 dresses altogether, how many days will each of them take to sew 48 dresses?

9. Simon takes 3 days and Lisa takes 1 day to paint $\frac{19}{20}$ of a house altogether. If Simon takes 4 days and Lisa takes 3 days to paint $1\frac{3}{5}$ houses altogether, how many days will each of them take to paint one house?

10. Ben takes 6 days to renovate a room and James takes 15 days to renovate the same room. If James starts renovating the room first and leaves the rest of the renovation to be completed by Ben, they will take 9 days to complete renovating the room. At this rate, how many days will Ben take to complete the job?

13 Data Analysis

Worked Example 1

The line graph below shows the amount of rainfall in a town over a six-day period.

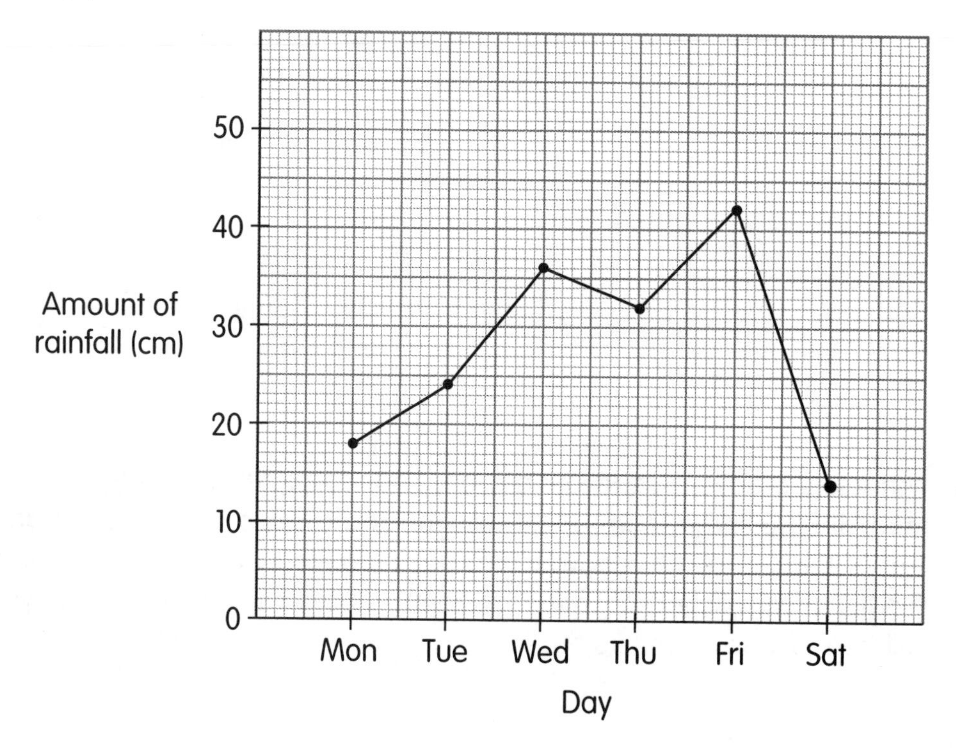

(a) What was the amount of rainfall on Wednesday?

(b) What was the greatest increase in the amount of rainfall between any two consecutive days?

(c) What was the greatest decrease in the amount of rainfall between any two consecutive days?

(a) The amount of rainfall on Wednesday was **36 cm**.

(b) To find the greatest increase in the amount of rainfall, locate the steepest upwards slope.
Steepest upwards slope ⟶ Tuesday to Wednesday
Greatest increase in the amount of rainfall = 36 cm – 24 cm
= 12 cm

The greatest increase in the amount of rainfall between any two consecutive days is **12 cm**.

(c) To find the greatest decrease in the amount of rainfall, locate the steepest downwards slope.
Steepest downwards slope ⟶ Friday to Saturday
Greatest decrease in the amount of rainfall = 42 cm – 14 cm
= 28 cm

The greatest decrease in the amount of rainfall between any two consecutive days is **28 cm**.

Practice Questions

Answer all questions.

1. The bar graph below shows the number of fans of 5 football clubs.

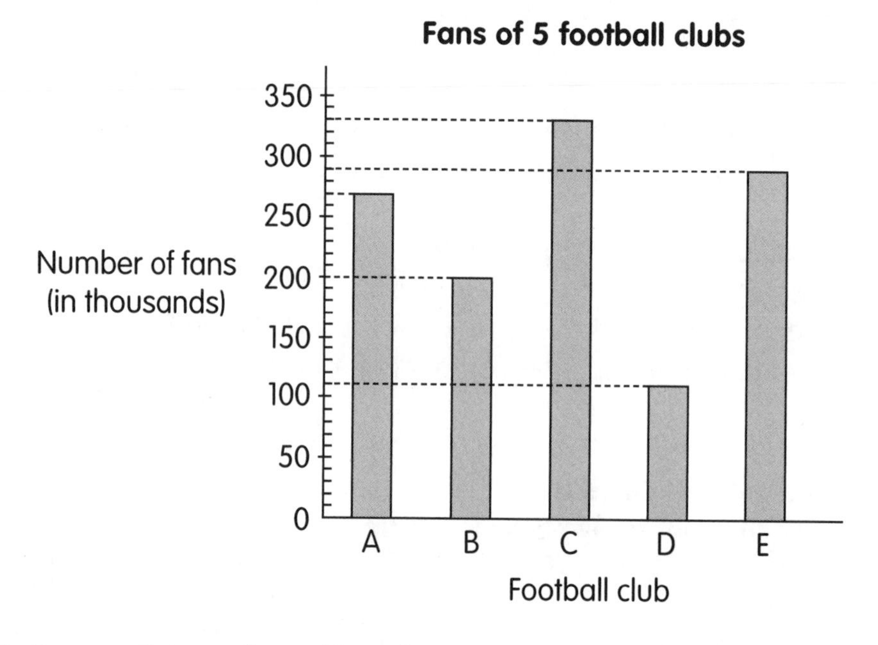

(a) Express the number of fans from club D as a percentage of the total number of fans from clubs D and E.

(b) If club C has 150,000 female fans, what is the ratio of the number of male fans to the number of female fans in club C?

(c) What is the average number of fans?

2. The line graph below shows Jessie's earnings in the last 5 months.

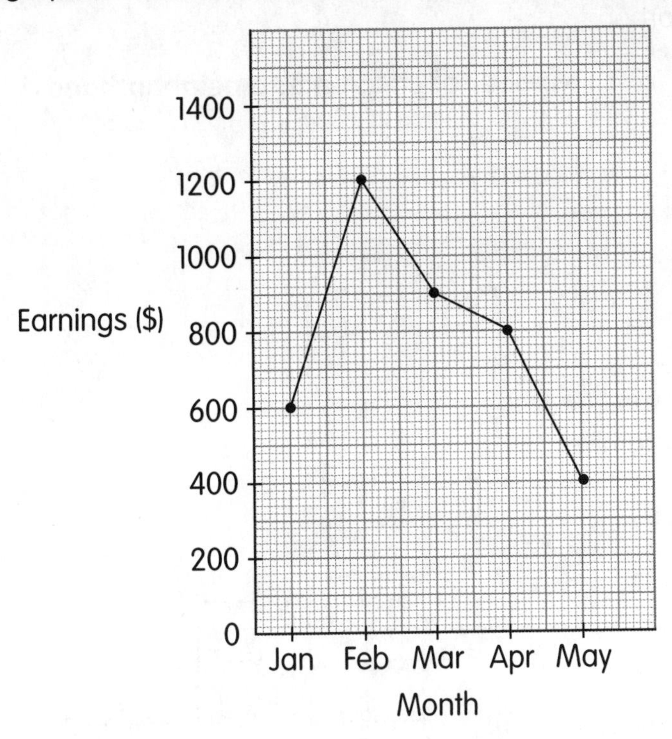

(a) How much more money did Jessie earn in February than in April?

(b) If Jessie saved $\frac{2}{5}$ of her January's earnings and $\frac{1}{3}$ of her February's earnings, how much money did she save?

(c) What was her average earnings from March to May?

3 . The histogram below shows the number of children each family has in a neighborhood.

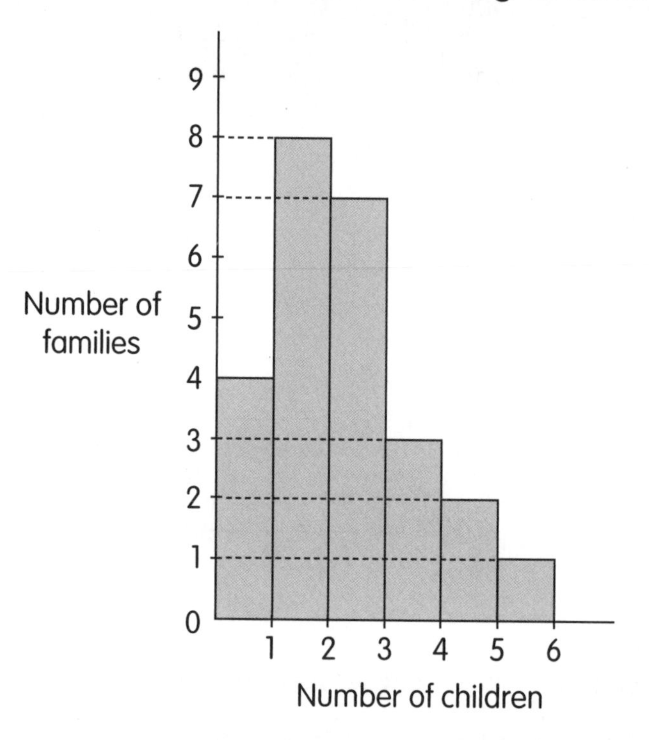

(a) What is the total number of families in the neighborhood?
(b) What percentage of the families have more than 3 children?
(c) Find the total number of children in the neighborhood.

4. The line graph below shows the number of stamps in 32 envelopes.

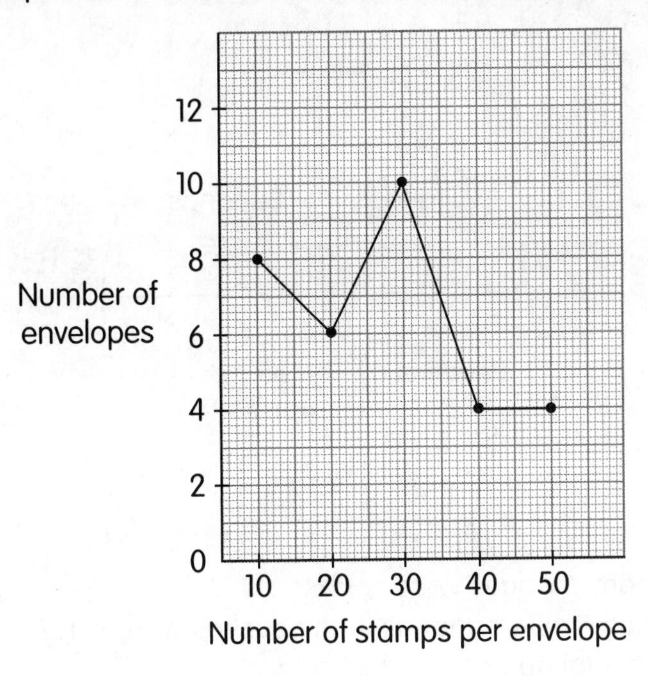

(a) How many envelopes contain less than 30 stamps?

(b) Pauline has some envelopes containing 40 stamps each. What would be the greatest possible number of stamps she could have?

(c) How many stamps are there altogether?

5. The pie chart below represents the number of fruits a fruit seller sold on a given day.

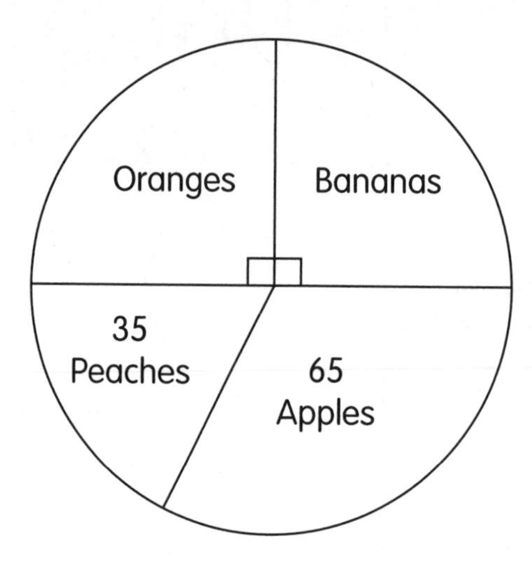

(a) How many oranges were sold?
(b) How many more bananas than peaches were sold?
(c) Find the total number of fruits sold.
(d) What percentage of the fruits sold were apples?

6. The pie chart below shows the number of different types of books sold at a bookstore.

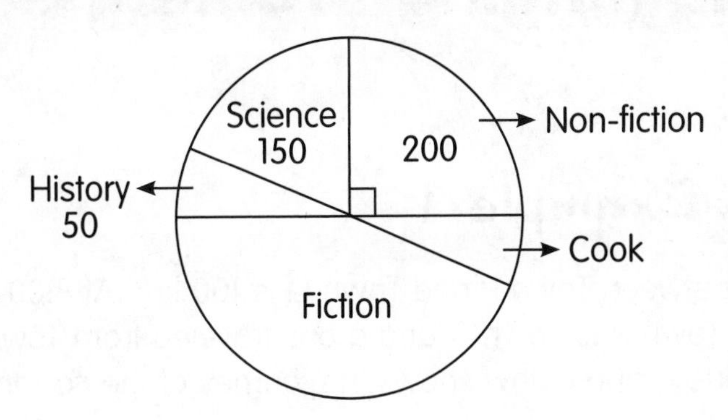

(a) The number of science and non-fiction books sold is equal to the number of fiction books sold. How many fiction books were sold?
(b) How many cook books were sold?
(c) What was the total number of books sold?
(d) What percentage of the books sold were non-fiction books?

7. I am thinking of six numbers that are less than 100. All the numbers are different. The mean of my six numbers is 12. What is the greatest possible number?

Worked Example 1

The distance between Town P and Town Q is 100 km. At 8:00 a.m., a car traveled from Town P to Town Q and a bus traveled from Town Q to Town P. The line graph below shows the journey of the car and the bus.

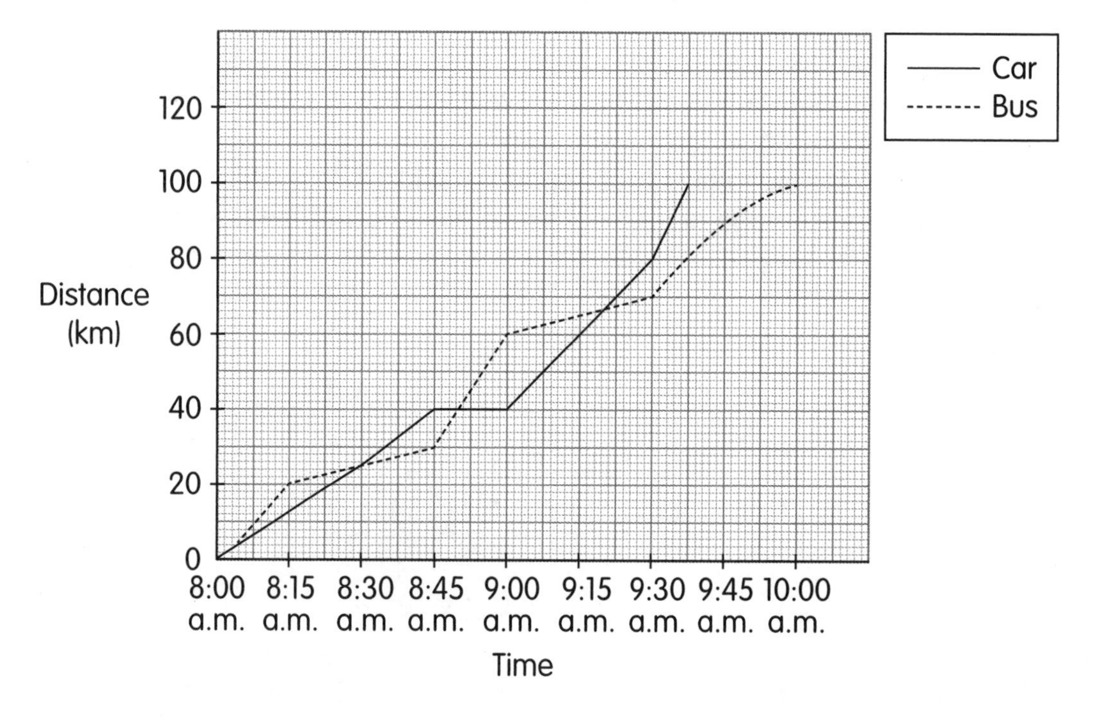

(a) How far away was the car from Town Q at 9:00 a.m.?

(b) How far apart were the car and the bus at 8:30 a.m.?

(c) At what time did the bus travel $\frac{1}{5}$ of the journey?

(a) Distance that the car had traveled at 9:00 a.m. = 40 km

Distance away from Town Q = 100 km – 40 km
= 60 km

The car was **60 km** away from Town Q at 9.00 a.m.

(b) At 8:30 a.m., the car had traveled 25 km from Town P.

At 8:30 a.m., the bus had traveled 25 km from Town Q.

Distance apart = 75 km – 25 km
= 50 km

The bus and the car were **50 km** apart at 8:30 a.m.

(c) $\frac{1}{5}$ of the journey ⟶ $\frac{1}{5} \times 100 = 20$ km

To know the time when the bus had traveled 20 km from Town Q, locate the time at the 80 km mark on the line graph.

The bus traveled $\frac{1}{5}$ of the journey at **8:15 a.m.**

Answer all questions.

1. The pie chart below represents the number of students who played in 4 different games.

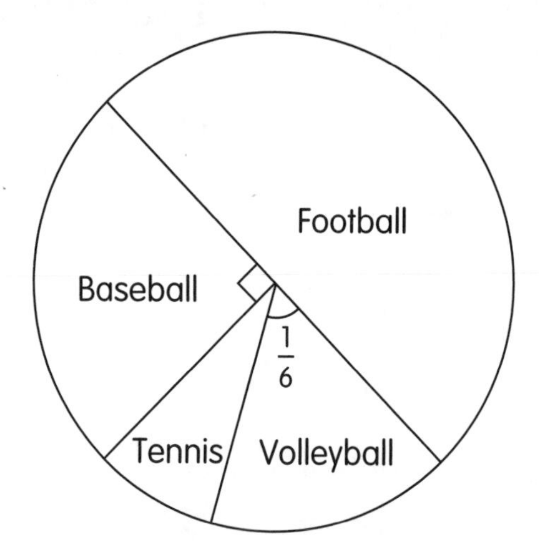

(a) What fraction of the students played tennis?
(b) If 42 students played volleyball, how many students played football?
(c) How many students played football and baseball?
(d) What percentage of the students played volleyball?

2. The distance between Town X and Town Y is 80 miles. At 7:00 a.m., a car traveled from Town X to Town Y and a truck traveled from Town Y to Town X. The line graph below shows the journey of the car and the truck.

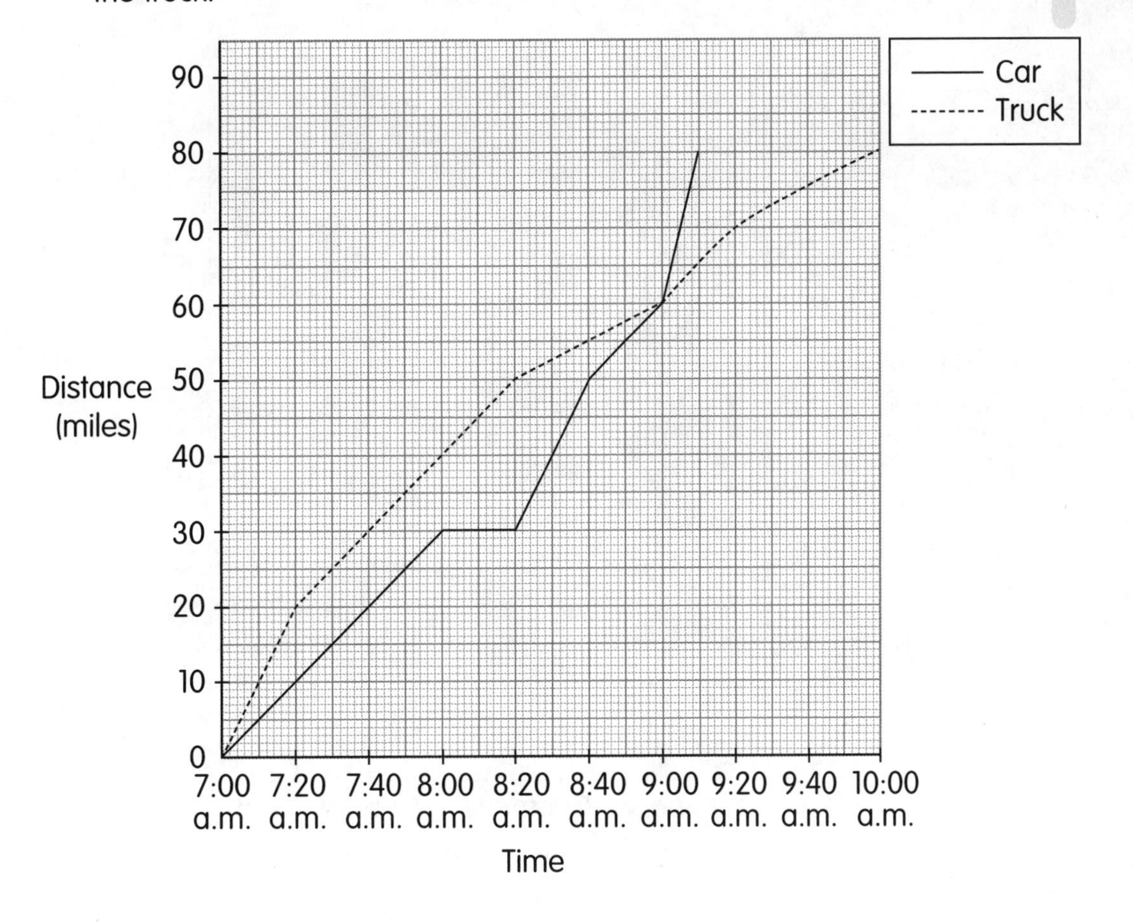

(a) How far away was the truck from Town X at 8:20 a.m.?

(b) At 8:40 a.m., how far away were the car and the truck from their destinations?

(c) At what time did the truck travel 75% of the journey?

3. The bar graph below shows the number of students who voted on their favorite and least favorite mathematics topics.

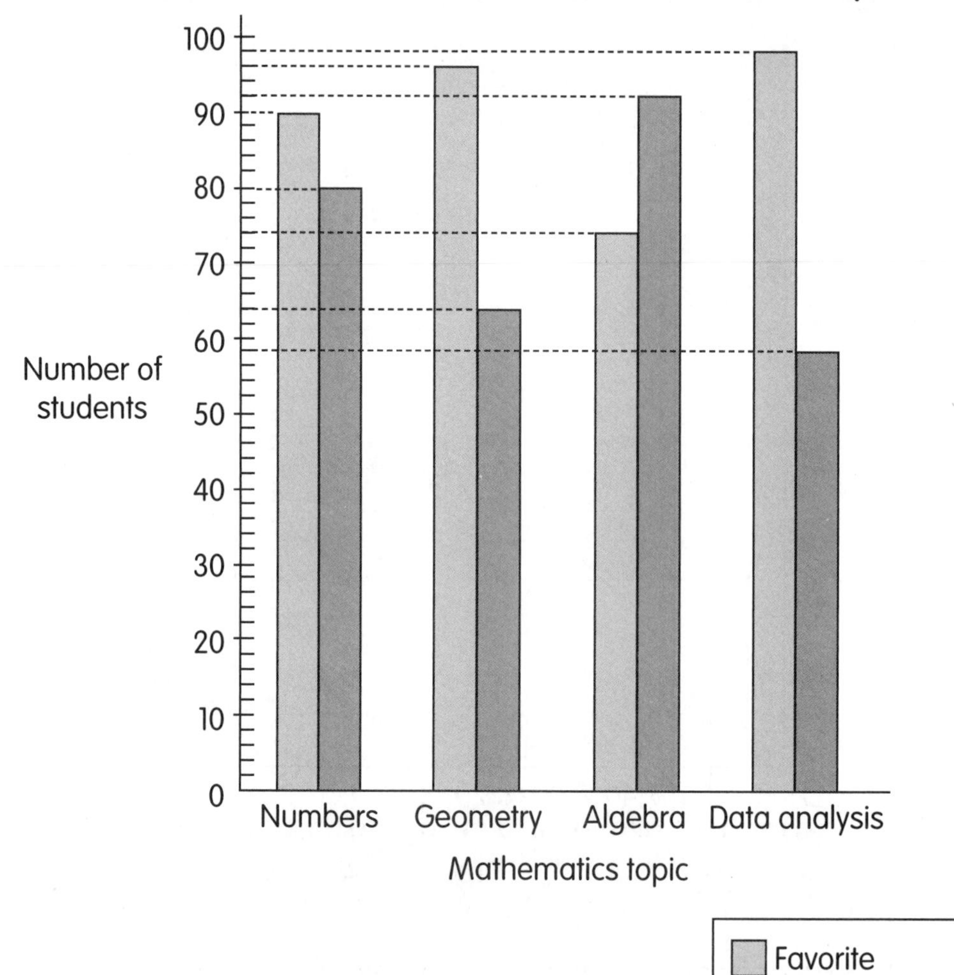

(a) Which topic was the most popular among the students?
(b) Which topic was the least popular among the students?
(c) Find the total number of students who chose algebra and geometry as their least favorite topics.
(d) Which topic had the second highest percentage of students who liked it?

4. A park is divided into 4 different sections, A, B, C, and D. The ratio of the area of section A to the area of section D is 1 : 2. The ratio of the area of section B to the area of section C is 5 : 3. The pie chart represents the area of each section.

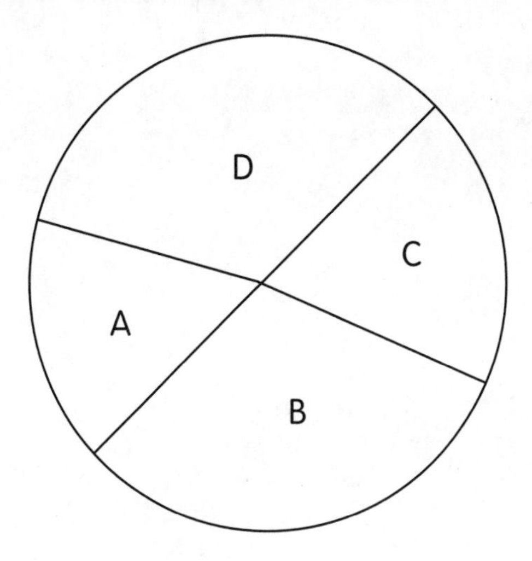

(a) What fraction of the park is section B?

(b) Section B is bigger than section A by 14 m^2. What is the area of the whole park?

5. A counting number is missing from the set of numbers below. If the mean and median are the same number, find the missing number.

8 4 9 3 ?

6. There are two groups of numbers, A and B. Matthew exchanged one number from group A with another number in group B. After the exchange, both group of numbers have the same mean. Find the two numbers.

8	6
2	5

Group A

9	3	5
3		4

Group B

14 Mixed Problems

Worked Example 1

A tank was $\frac{3}{4}$-filled with fuel. When $\frac{1}{3}$ of the fuel was left, Scott poured in 450 gallons of fuel to fill up the tank. How many gallons of fuel can the tank contain?

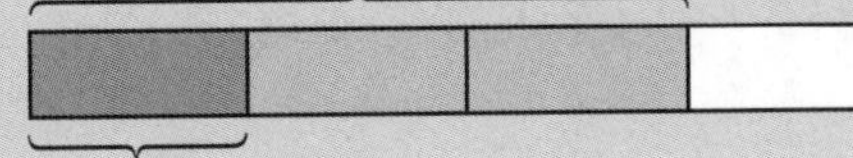

To fill up the tank, Scott pours in 3 units of fuel.

3 units ⟶ 450
1 unit ⟶ $450 \div 3 = 150$
4 units ⟶ $4 \times 150 = 600$

The tank can contain **600** gallons of fuel.

Answer all questions.

1. If Beth gave $1 to Ruth, Ruth would have twice as much as Beth. If Ruth gave $1 to Beth, they would have the same amount of money. How much did each of them have?

2. Sally thinks of a number. When she multiplies the number by itself and then adds 10.01, she gets 91.01. What is Sally's number?

3. When a whole number is multiplied by another whole number, the product is 377. What are the two numbers?

4. Betty and Joshua had $200 in all. After Betty spent $50 and Joshua lost $80, they each had the same amount of money. How much did Joshua have at first?

5. The table below shows the number of short-sighted and long-sighted boys and girls. Complete the table.

	Short-sighted	Long-sighted	Total
Number of boys	32		
Number of girls			53
Total		44	104

6. A piece of paper measuring 32 cm by 16 cm is cut into half. Each of the pieces is cut into half again. The process is repeated until a piece measuring 2 cm by 1 cm is obtained. How many cuts are needed in all?

7. The solid below is made up of 6 identical cubes. Each cube has a side of 5 cm. What is the total surface area of the solid?

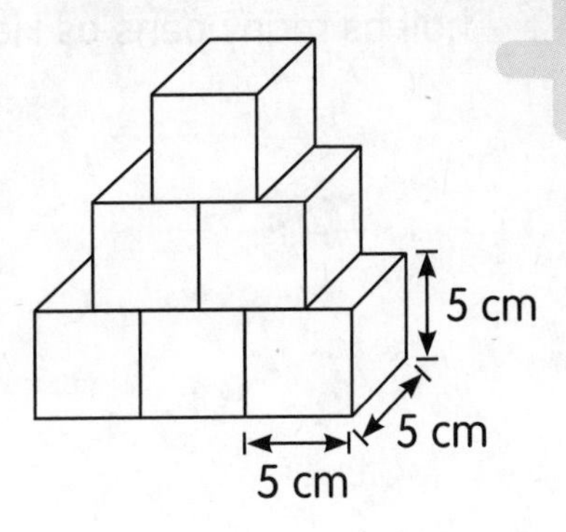

8. Sam puts 14 coins into 4 different rows. The first row has 3 more coins than the second row. The second row has 1 coin less than the third row. The fourth row has twice as many coins as the second row. Find the number of coins in each row.

9. The ratio of the number of Henry's pens to the number of Donald's pens was 3 : 5. After Donald gave away 35 pens to a charity, he had half as many pens as Henry. How many pens did Donald have at first?

10. The ratio of the area of Triangle P to the area of Triangle Q is 2 : 1. The ratio of the area of the shaded region to the area of the unshaded region is 1 : 1. Find the ratio of the area of Triangle Q to area of the unshaded region.

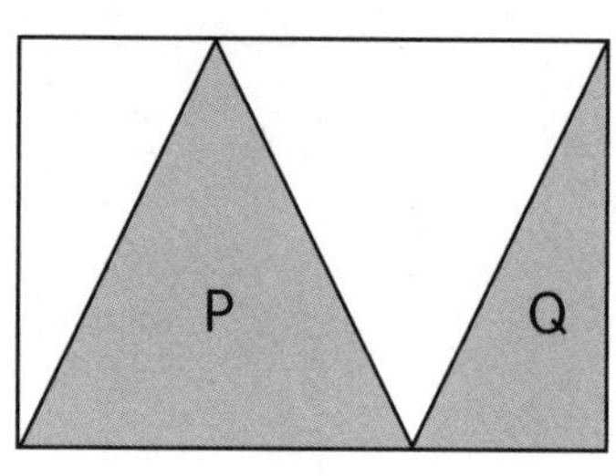

Challenging Problems

Worked Example 1

In the figure below, PQRS is a rectangle and TPR is a triangle. If the ratio of the length of ST to the length of TR is 1 : 2, what is the ratio of the area of triangle TPR to the area of rectangle PQRS?

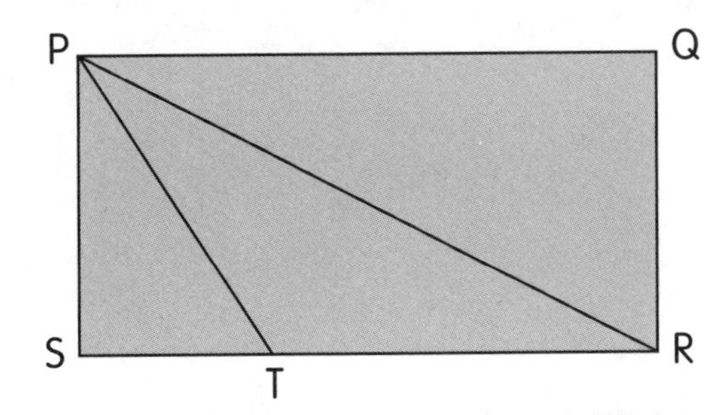

Since the ratio of the length of ST to the length of TR is 1 : 2, the length of SR is 3 units. Let the length of the rectangle be 3 units and the width of the rectangle be QR.

Area of rectangle PQRS = $3 \times QR$

Since the ratio of the length of ST to the length of TR is 1 : 2, the length of TR is 2 units. Let the base of the triangle be 2 units and the height of the triangle be QR.

Area of triangle TPR = $\frac{1}{2} \times 2 \times QR$
= QR

The ratio of the area of triangle TPR to the area of rectangle PQRS is **1 : 3**.

Answer all questions.

1. There are thirteen cards numbered 1 to 13. Tracy picks up three cards and finds that when the numbers on the cards are multiplied together, the product is 252. Which are the three cards?

2. Brian is given a list of clues to solve a 5-digit number puzzle.

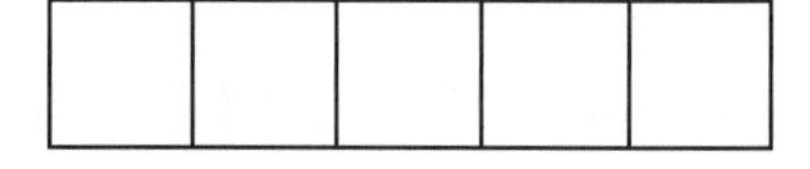

The clues are:
(i) All the digits are different.
(ii) The first digit is an odd number and it is greater than the third digit.
(iii) The fourth digit is three times the value of the first digit.
(iv) The last digit is the product of the second and third digits.

What is the number?

3. In a family, the girls have twice as many sisters as brothers. The boys have five times as many sisters as brothers. How many boys and girls are there?

4. Alan and Amy want to buy a pen. Alan needs 50¢ more and Amy needs 10¢ more. When they put their money together, they still do not have enough money to buy the pen. Assume that there are only 5¢, 10¢, 20¢, and 50¢ coins, how much does the pen cost?

5. Karen has a rectangular cardboard measuring 38 cm long and 27 cm wide. If she needs to cut some small rectangles, each 5 cm long and 3 cm wide, from the cardboard, how many small rectangles can she get?

6. The figure below shows a rectangular garden measuring 21 m by 15 m. Robert plans to lay square tiles measuring 1.5 m by 1.5 m on the shaded path. How many such tiles will he need?

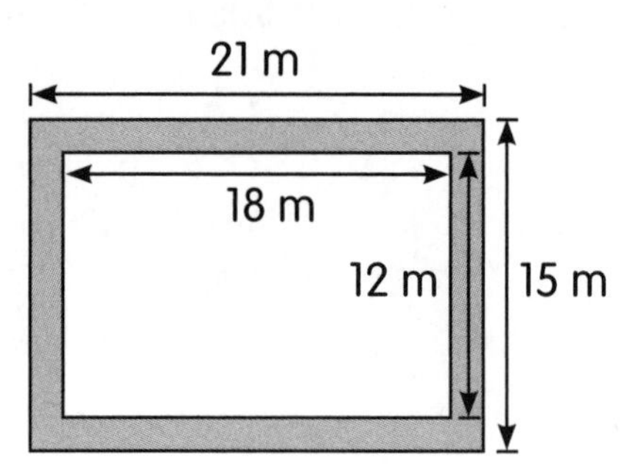

7. Paul is twice as old as Timothy this year. If their combined age is 54 years, what will be their combined age when Timothy is as old as Paul is this year?

8. Smith packed 8 apples into each basket and 20 apples into each box. If 560 apples were packed into 46 baskets and boxes altogether, find the greatest number of boxes that he had.

9. Sandy divided a 2-digit number by another 2-digit number and obtained 0.78125 as the answer. Find the two numbers.

10. There are 32 tennis players in a tennis tournament. If a player loses, he will be out of the tournament. If a player wins, he will proceed to the next round. How many matches did Terence play if he wins the tournament?

1 Whole Numbers

Practice Questions (pp. 3–6)

1. **Method 1**

Aaron	Cathy	Esther	Ginny	Ian	Karen
1	2	3	4	5	6
7	8	9	10	11	12
⋮	⋮	⋮	⋮	⋮	⋮
97	98	99	100		

Ginny gets the last sticker from Mr. Lee.
Method 2
To determine who gets the last sticker, look at the remainder (R) obtained when the number of stickers is divided by 6 people.
$100 \div 6 = 16$ R 4
The last sticker will go to the 4th person in the circle.
Ginny gets the last sticker from Mr. Lee.

2. 27
3. If there is no CD left over, least possible number of CDs $= 2 \times 3 \times 5$
$= 30$
Since there is always 1 CD left over, the least possible number of CDs Louis could have is $= 30 + 1$
$= 31$
4. Page numbers that contain the digit 2: 2, 12, 20, 21, 22, 23, 24, 25, 26, 27, 28, 29, 32, 42, 52, 62, 72, 82, 92
Page numbers that contain the digit 2 but not divisible by 2: 21, 23, 25, 27, and 29.
5 page numbers contain the digit 2 but are not divisible by 2.
5. 49 moves
6. (a) She threw 6 darts.
(b) Accept all correct answers. For e.g. 19, 19, 19, 19, 12, and 12
7. Number of games played in all
$= 5 + 4 + 3 + 2 + 1$
$= 15$
8. Difference $= 502 - 397$
$= 105$
New sum $= 2783 + 105$
$= 2888$
9. Bag P [12][ ]

Bag Q [12][ ][12][ ][12][ ]
66

2 units → $66 - (12 \times 3) = 30$
1 unit → $30 \div 2 = 15$
Number of toys she added into each bag $= 15$

10. Joseph [28][ ]

Sarah [28][ ][28][ ][28][ ][28][ ]
157

3 units → $157 - (28 \times 4) = 45$
1 unit → $45 \div 3 = 15$
Number of magnets added $= 15$

11. Olivia [32][ ]

Sally [32][ ][32][ ][32][ ]
154

2 units → $154 - (32 \times 3) = 58$
Number of stamps they bought in all $= 58$

Challenging Problems (pp. 8–11)

1. Number X $= (16 \times$ Number Y$) + 3$

[X]

[Y] … [Y][3]
16 units

Let [Y] be 1 unit.
Number Y = 1 unit
Number X = 16 units + 3
16 units + 3 + 1 unit + 16 + 3 → 345
17 units → 323
1 unit → $323 \div 17$
$= 19$
Number X $= (16 \times 19) + 3$
$= 307$

2. Next palindromic number after 12,321
$= 12{,}421$
$12{,}421 - 12{,}321 = 100$
His speed $= 100 \div 2$
$= 50$ km/h
3. $770 = 2 \times 5 \times 7 \times 11$
Since the ages are those of two adults, their possible ages are $2 \times 11 = 22$ and $5 \times 7 = 35$.
Sum of their ages $= 22 + 35$
$= 57$ years
4.
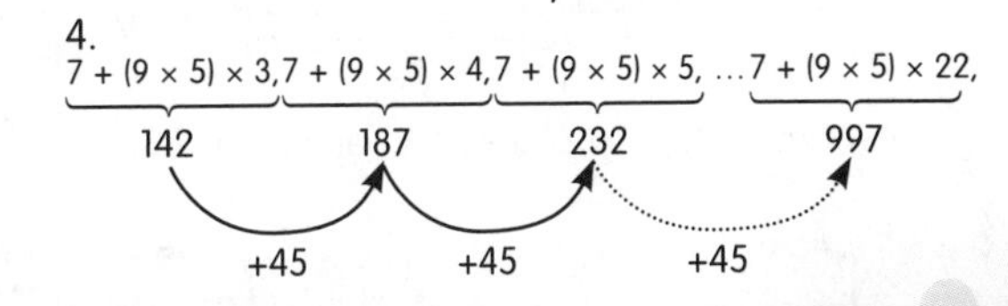

The numbers are 142, 187, ..., 952 and 997.
Numbers of 3-digit numbers = 22 – 3 + 1
= 20

5. 1st candidate
2nd candidate 8
3rd candidate 13
4th candidate 15
240

8 + 13 + 15 = 36
4 units ⟶ 240 + 36 = 276
1 unit ⟶ 276 ÷ 4 = 69
Lowest number of votes received by a candidate = 69 – 15
= 54

6. $49

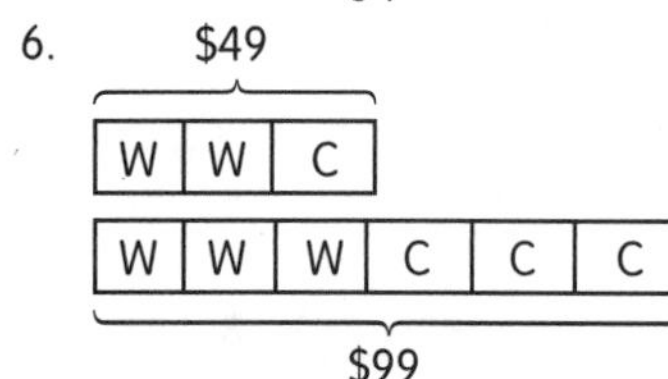

$99

Cost of one watch and one calculator
= $99 ÷ 3
= $33
Cost of one watch = $49 – $33
= $16

7. $100

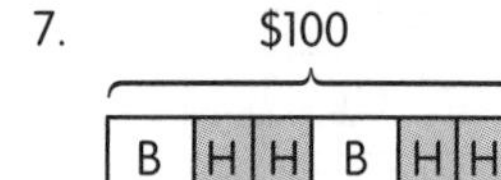

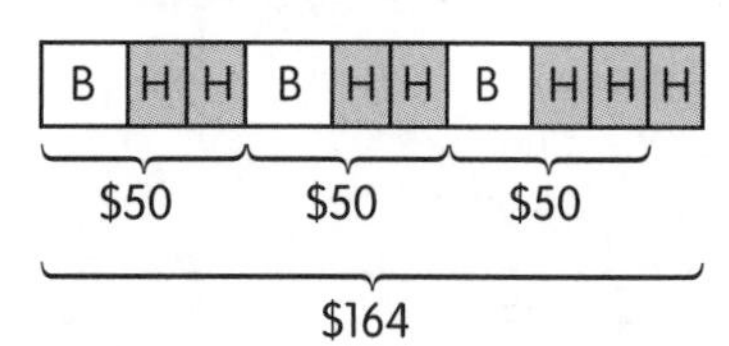

$50 $50 $50

$164

Cost of one bag and two hats = $100 ÷ 2
= $50
Cost of three bags and six hats = 3 × $50
= $150
Cost of one hat = $164 – $150
= $14

8. 8 watches and 8 lamps
= $176 + $208 = $384

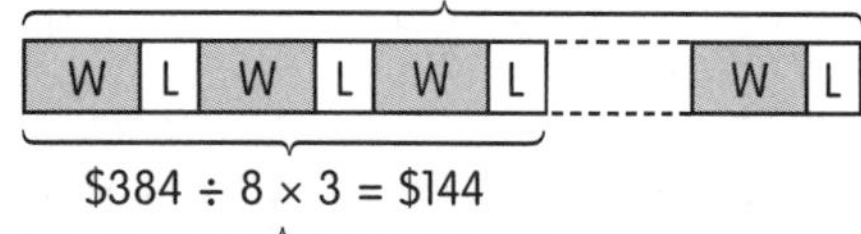

$384 ÷ 8 × 3 = $144

$176

Cost of eight watches and eight lamps
= $176 + $208
= $384
Cost of one watch and one lamp
= $384 ÷ 8
= $48
Cost of three watches and three lamps
= 3 × $48
= $144
Cost of two lamps = $176 – $144
= $32
Cost of one lamp = $32 ÷ 2
= $16

9. 1 mug

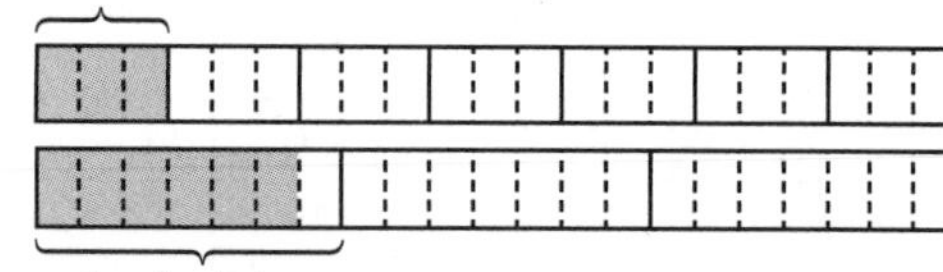

1 calculator
4 □ ⟶ $12
1 □ ⟶ $12 ÷ 4 = $3
3 □ ⟶ 3 × $3 = $9
Cost of one mug = $9

10. 1 jacket

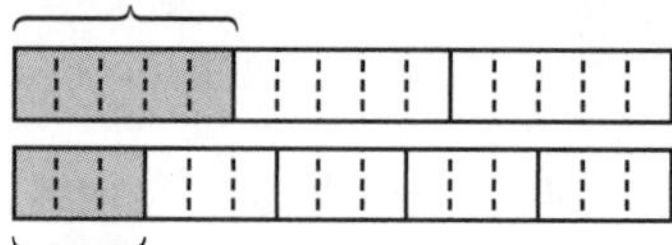

1 shirt
2 □ ⟶ $16
1 □ ⟶ $16 ÷ 2 = $8
3 □ ⟶ 3 × $8 = $24
Cost of one shirt = $24

2 Fractions

Practice Questions (pp. 14–17)

1. $1\frac{1}{12}$ kg
2. $13\frac{17}{20}$ cm
3. $1\frac{1}{5}$ km
4. **Method 1**

$2\frac{1}{3}$ cm + $2\frac{1}{3}$ cm + $2\frac{1}{3}$ cm = 7 cm
A 7-cm strip of paper yields 3 smaller pieces.
7 cm ⟶ 3 pieces
21 cm ⟶ 3 × 3 = 9 pieces
Number of pieces Tommy will have = 9

Method 2

$2\frac{1}{3} = \frac{7}{3}$
Number of pieces Tommy will have = $21 \div \frac{7}{3}$
$= 21 \times \frac{3}{7}$
$= 9$

5. bag of flour

Right pan

Left pan

bag of rice   1-kg weight

1 unit → 1 kg
2 units → 2 × 1 kg = 2 kg
Weight of two bags of flour = 2 × 2 kg
= 4 kg

6. book   candy $2

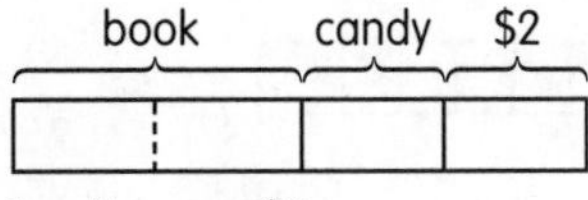

1 unit → $2
2 units → 2 × $2 = $4
Amount of money Sam paid for the book
= $4

7. **Method 1**
television set

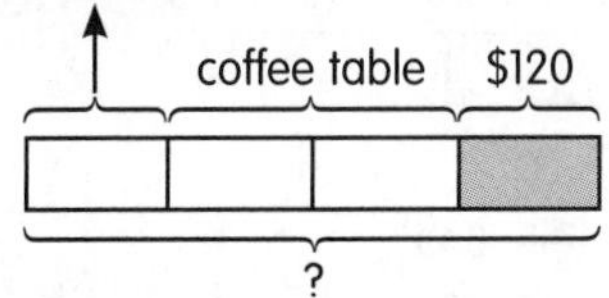

1 unit → $120
4 units → 4 × $120 = $480

Method 2
Remainder = $1 - \frac{1}{4}$
$= \frac{3}{4}$

Fraction saved = $\frac{1}{3} \times \frac{3}{4}$
$= \frac{1}{4}$ of sum of money

$\frac{1}{4}$ of sum of money = $120
Amount of money Mr. Rafik had at first
= 4 × $120
= $480

8. **Method 1**
lawn mower   barbecue grill

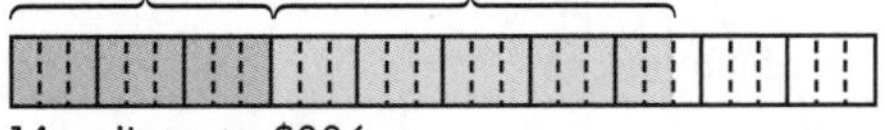

14 units → $336
1 unit → $336 ÷ 14 = $24
9 units → 9 × $24 = $216
Amount of money paid for the lawn mower
= $216

Method 2
Fraction of money left after buying lawn mower = $1 - \frac{3}{10}$
$= \frac{7}{10}$

Fraction of money spent on barbecue grill
$= \frac{2}{3} \times \frac{7}{10}$
$= \frac{14}{30}$
$= \frac{7}{15}$

$\frac{7}{15}$ of his money → $336
$\frac{1}{15}$ of his money → $336 ÷ 7 = $48
$\frac{15}{15}$ of his money → 15 × $48 = $720
Amount of money paid for the lawn mower
$= \frac{3}{10} \times \$720$
= $216

9. **Method 1**
shirt   book   ?

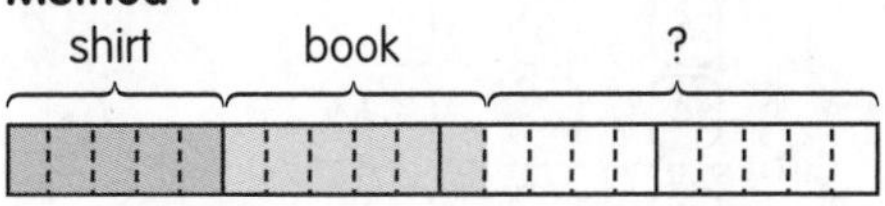

(a) Fraction of his allowance left = $\frac{9}{20}$
(b) 6 units → $18
1 unit → $18 ÷ 6 = $3
20 units → 20 × $3 = $60
Amount of allowance he had at first
= $60

Method 2

$\frac{3}{4}$ of remainder — $\frac{2}{5}$ on a book / $\frac{3}{5}$ left

(a) Fraction of his allowance left after buying a shirt = $1 - \frac{1}{4}$
$= \frac{3}{4}$

Fraction of his allowance left after buying a shirt and a book = $\frac{3}{5} \times \frac{3}{4}$
$= \frac{9}{20}$

(b) Fraction of his allowance spent on a book = $\frac{2}{5} \times \frac{3}{4}$
$= \frac{6}{20}$

$\frac{6}{20}$ of his allowance → $18
$\frac{1}{20}$ of his allowance → $18 ÷ 6 = $3
$\frac{20}{20}$ of his allowance → 20 × $3 = $60
Amount of allowance he had at first = $60

10. $\frac{2}{5} = \frac{4}{10}$

red green blue

yellow

Difference between number of red marbles and number of blue marbles = 1 unit

1 unit ⟶ 17

10 units ⟶ 10 × 17 = 170

Total number of marbles = 170

Challenging Problems (pp. 20–24)

1. B. $\frac{7}{36}$

2. (a) $\frac{4}{6} - \frac{2}{8} = \frac{5}{12}$

   (b) $\frac{4}{8} - \frac{2}{6} = \frac{1}{6}$

3. $\frac{N}{D} = \frac{2}{3}$; N × D = 216

   216 = 2 × 2 × 2 × 3 × 3 × 3

   $\frac{N}{D} = \frac{2}{3} \times (\frac{2}{3} \times \frac{3}{2}) = \frac{12}{18}$

4. Jim

   Shirley

   gave to Shirley

   260

   52

   8 units ⟶ 260 − 52 = 208

   1 unit ⟶ 208 ÷ 8 = 26

   Jim gave 26 coins to Shirley.

   4 units ⟶ 4 × 26 = 104

   Number of coins Shirley had at first

   = 104 + (52 − 26)

   = 130

5. 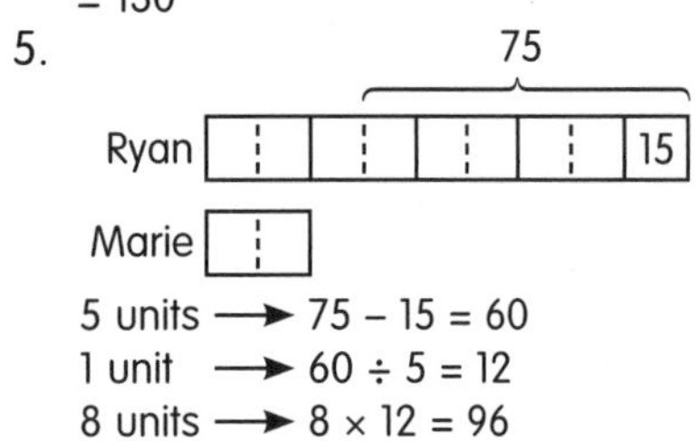

   5 units ⟶ 75 − 15 = 60

   1 unit ⟶ 60 ÷ 5 = 12

   8 units ⟶ 8 × 12 = 96

   Number of marbles Ryan had at first

   = 96 + 15

   = 111

6. Kevin

   Ruth

   $115

   Bob

   Ruth

   $130

   1 unit ⟶ $130 − $115 = $15

   2 units ⟶ 2 × $15 = $30

   Amount of money Ruth has

   = $115 − $30

   = $85

7. Steve

   Larry

   171

   39

   10 units ⟶ 171 + 39 = 210

   1 unit ⟶ 210 ÷ 10 = 21

   7 units ⟶ 7 × 21 = 147

   Number of marbles Steve has = 147

8. Farm A

   Farm B

   845

   13 units ⟶ 845

   1 unit ⟶ 845 ÷ 13 = 65

   8 units ⟶ 8 × 65 = 520

   Number of sheep in Farm B = 520

9. 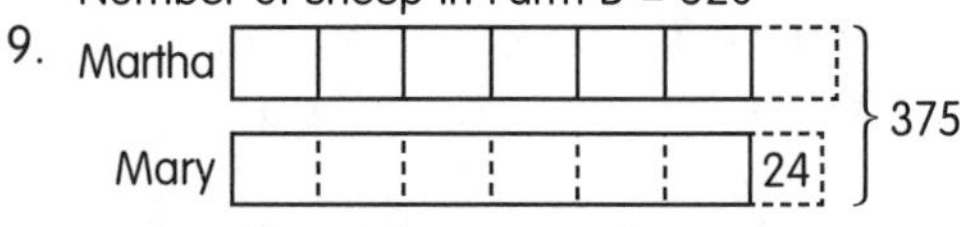

   13 units ⟶ 375 − 24 = 351

   1 unit ⟶ 351 ÷ 13 = 27

   7 units ⟶ 7 × 27 = 189

   6 units ⟶ 6 × 27 = 162

   Number of jelly beans Martha had = 189

   Number of jelly beans Mary had = 162 + 24

   = 186

10. In 1 h, the first man can complete $\frac{1}{6}$ of the task, the second man can complete $\frac{1}{4}$ of the task, and the third man can complete $\frac{1}{3}$ of the task.

    In 1 h, all three men can complete

    $= \frac{1}{6} + \frac{1}{4} + \frac{1}{3}$

    $= \frac{9}{12}$

    $= \frac{3}{4}$ of the task.

    $\frac{3}{4}$ of the task ⟶ 1 h

    $\frac{1}{4}$ of the task ⟶ $1 \div 3 = \frac{1}{3}$ h

$\frac{4}{4}$ of the task → $4 \times \frac{1}{3} = \frac{4}{3}$

$= 1\frac{1}{3}$ h

The three men will take $1\frac{1}{3}$ h to complete the task.

3 Area and Perimeter

Practice Questions (pp. 28–31)

1. 374 cm^2
2. 4 rectangles
3. Number of 10-cm square tiles needed
   $= \frac{600 \times 800}{10 \times 10}$
   $= 4800$
4. Length of one side of the square
   $= 32$ m $\div 4$
   $= 8$ m
   Area of square floor = 8 m × 8 m
   = 64 m^2
   Cost of carpeting the floor = 64 × \$8
   = \$512
5. Width + length of rectangle = 50 cm ÷ 2
   = 25 cm
   Width of rectangle = 25 cm − 16 cm
   = 9 cm
   Area of rectangle = 16 cm × 9 cm
   = 144 cm^2
   Area of square = 144 cm^2
   = 12 cm × 12 cm
   Length of the square = 12 cm
6. Width [1 unit]
   Length [3 units]
   } 72 cm ÷ 2 = 36 cm

   4 units → 36 cm
   1 unit → 36 cm ÷ 4 = 9 cm
   3 units → 3 × 9 cm = 27 cm
   Area of rectangle = 27 cm × 9 cm
   = 243 cm^2
7. Area of outer rectangle = 40 m × 30 m
   = 1200 m^2
   Length of inner rectangle
   = 40 m − 5 m − 5 m
   = 30 m
   Width of inner rectangle
   = 30 m − 5 m − 5 m
   = 20 m
   Area of inner rectangle = 30 m × 20 m
   = 600 m^2
   Area of path = 1200 m^2 − 600 m^2
   = 600 m^2
8. 
   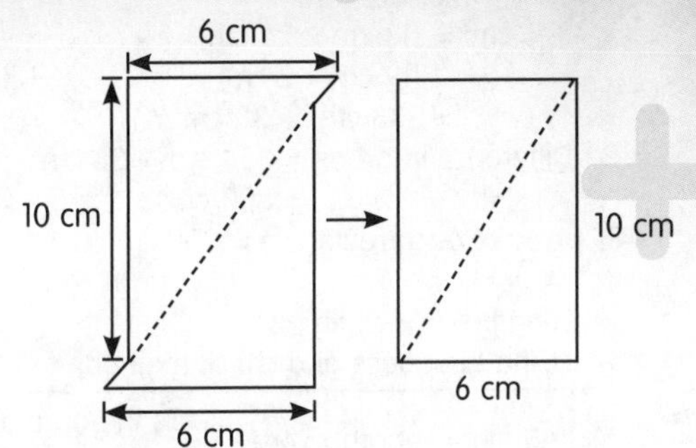

   Area = 10 cm × 6 cm
   = 60 cm^2
9. Area of one rectangle = 25 cm × 8 cm
   = 200 cm^2
   Area of figure = Area of two rectangles − Area of middle square
   = (2 × 200 cm^2) − (8 cm × 8 cm)
   = 400 cm^2 − 64 cm^2
   = 336 cm^2
10. Along the length of the land, there are 55 ÷ 5 = 11 intervals of 5 m each. Therefore, he can plant 11 + 1 = 12 trees.
    Along the width of the land, there are 30 ÷ 5 = 6 intervals of 5 m each. Therefore, he can plant 6 + 1 = 7 trees.
    At each corner, the same tree lies along each length and width; so, there are a total of 4 trees shared by both lengths and widths.
    Number of trees he can plant
    = 2 × (12 + 7) − 4
    = 34

Challenging Problems (pp. 34–38)

1. 425 cm^2
2. 44 cm
3. 6 rectangles
4. 24 rectangles
5. Divide one side of the square into 5 cm and 7 cm and the other side of the square into 4 cm and 8 cm.
6. Two square numbers, which has a difference of 80, are 64 and 144.
   64 cm^2 = 8 cm × 8 cm
   144 cm^2 = 12 cm × 12 cm
   Perimeter of figure
   = 12 cm + 12 cm + 12 cm + 8 cm + 8 cm + 8 cm + 4 cm
   = 64 cm
7. There are 2 possible answers.
   376 cm^2 = (13 cm × 7 cm) + (19 cm × 15 cm)
   = 91 cm^2 + 285 cm^2
   Difference in areas = 285 cm^2 − 91 cm^2
   = 194 cm^2

$376\ cm^2 = (13\ cm \times 26\ cm) + (19\ cm \times 2\ cm)$
$= 338\ cm^2 + 38\ cm^2$
Difference in areas $= 338\ cm^2 - 38\ cm^2$
$= 300\ cm^2$

8. Area of each rectangle $= 200\ cm^2 \div 4$
$= 50\ cm^2$
Length $= 2 \times$ width
Using the guess and check method,

Width (cm)	Length (cm)	Area (cm^2)	Is the area of each rectangle $50\ cm^2$?
3	6	18	No.
4	8	32	No.
5	**10**	**50**	**Yes.**

Method 1
Perimeter $= 4 \times (10\ cm + 5\ cm + 5\ cm)$
$= 80\ cm$
Method 2
Perimeter $= 5\ cm + 5\ cm + 10\ cm + 5\ cm + 5\ cm + 10\ cm + 5\ cm + 5\ cm + 10\ cm + 5\ cm + 5\ cm + 10\ cm$
$= 80\ cm$

9. $20\ cm^2$

10. Length of figure = 8 widths of a rectangle
= 5 lengths of a rectangle
Width of figure = 1 length + 1 width
$= 1$ length $+ \frac{5}{8}$ length
$= \frac{13}{8}$ lengths
Area of figure $= 5$ lengths $\times \frac{13}{8}$ lengths
$= 5 \times \frac{13}{8}$ length $\times$ length
$= \frac{65}{8} \times$ length $\times$ length
$= 520\ cm^2$
Length $\times$ length $= \frac{520 \times 8}{65}$
$= 64\ cm^2$
$= 8\ cm \times 8\ cm$
Length of rectangle $= 8\ cm$
Perimeter of figure
$= (5$ lengths $+ \frac{13}{8}$ lengths$) \times 2$
$= [(5 \times 8\ cm) + (\frac{13}{8} \times 8\ cm)] \times 2$
$= 106\ cm$

4 Area of Triangles

Practice Questions (pp. 44–48)

1. $30\ cm^2$
2. 8 triangles
3. AE is the base of triangles ABE, ACE, and ADE. Since BD is parallel to AE, triangles ABE, ACE, and ADE have the same height. Since triangles ABE, ACE, and ADE have the same base and height, they have the same area.
4. Area of figure
$= 2 \times$ Area of triangle XYZ
$= 2 \times [\frac{1}{2} \times 18\ cm \times (10\ cm \div 2)]$
$= 90\ cm^2$
5. Area of shaded region
$= (\frac{1}{2} \times 20\ cm \times 11\ cm) - (\frac{1}{2} \times 20\ cm \times 5\ cm)$
$= 110\ cm^2 - 50\ cm^2$
$= 60\ cm^2$
6. **Method 1**
Area of rectangle $= 10\ cm \times 12\ cm$
$= 120\ cm^2$
Area of unshaded triangle
$= \frac{1}{2} \times 4\ cm \times 12\ cm$
$= 24\ cm^2$
Area of shaded region $= 120\ cm^2 - 24\ cm^2$
$= 96\ cm^2$
Method 2
Divide the shaded region into two triangles.
Area of shaded region
$= (\frac{1}{2} \times 6\ cm \times 12\ cm) + (\frac{1}{2} \times 10\ cm \times 12\ cm)$
$= 36\ cm^2 + 60\ cm^2$
$= 96\ cm^2$
7. **Method 1**
Area of unshaded region
$= (\frac{1}{2} \times 17\ cm \times 17\ cm) + (\frac{1}{2} \times 9\ cm \times 17\ cm)$
$= 144\frac{1}{2}\ cm^2 + 76\frac{1}{2}\ cm^2$
$= 221\ cm^2$
Method 2
Area of unshaded region
$= (17\ cm \times 17\ cm) - (\frac{1}{2} \times (17\ cm - 9\ cm) \times 17\ cm)$
$= 289\ cm^2 - 68\ cm^2$
$= 221\ cm^2$
8. Area of triangle AEF
= area of square ABCD – area of triangle ABE – area of triangle ADF – area of triangle ECF
$= (12\ cm \times 12\ cm) - (\frac{1}{2} \times 12\ cm \times 6\ cm) - (\frac{1}{2} \times 12\ cm \times 6\ cm) - (\frac{1}{2} \times 6\ cm \times 6\ cm)$
$= 144\ cm^2 - 36\ cm^2 - 36\ cm^2 - 18\ cm^2$
$= 54\ cm^2$
9. Area of square $= 7\ cm \times 7\ cm$
$= 49\ cm^2$

Area of two small unshaded triangles
$= 2 \times (\frac{1}{2} \times 2 \text{ cm} \times 2 \text{ cm})$
$= 4 \text{ cm}^2$
Area of two large unshaded triangles
$= 2 \times (\frac{1}{2} \times 5 \text{ cm} \times 5 \text{ cm})$
$= 25 \text{ cm}^2$
Area of shaded region
$= 49 \text{ cm}^2 - 4 \text{ cm}^2 - 25 \text{ cm}^2$
$= 20 \text{ cm}^2$

10. **Method 1**
Perimeter of figure
$= 30 \text{ cm} + 12 \text{ cm} + 25 \text{ cm} + 13 \text{ cm}$
$= 80 \text{ cm}$
Area of figure
$= (25 \text{ cm} \times 12 \text{ cm}) + (\frac{1}{2} \times (30 \text{ cm} - 25 \text{ cm}) \times 12 \text{ cm})$
$= 300 \text{ cm}^2 + 30 \text{ cm}^2$
$= 330 \text{ cm}^2$
Method 2
Form a new rectangle by creating another identical figure.

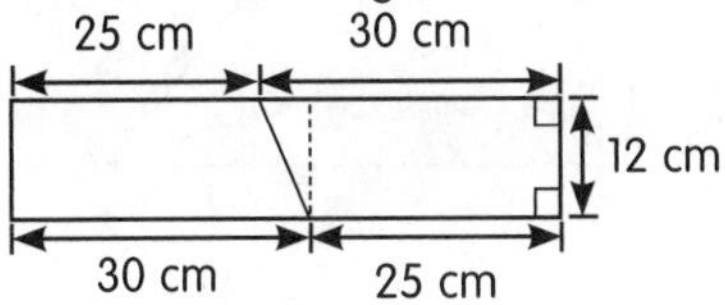

Area of figure $= \frac{1}{2} \times$ area of new rectangle
$= \frac{1}{2} \times (30 \text{ cm} + 25 \text{ cm}) \times 12 \text{ cm}$
$= 330 \text{ cm}^2$

Challenging Problems (pp. 51–56)

1. Area of triangle ABC $= \frac{1}{2} \times 8 \text{ cm} \times 8 \text{ cm}$
$= 32 \text{ cm}^2$
Area of triangle AEF
$= \frac{1}{2} \times (8 \text{ cm} + 6 \text{ cm}) \times 6 \text{ cm}$
$= 42 \text{ cm}^2$
Area of shaded region
$= (8 \text{ cm} \times 8 \text{ cm}) + (6 \text{ cm} \times 6 \text{ cm}) - 32 \text{ cm}^2 - 42 \text{ cm}^2$
$= 64 \text{ cm}^2 + 36 \text{ cm}^2 - 32 \text{ cm}^2 - 42 \text{ cm}^2$
$= 26 \text{ cm}^2$

2.

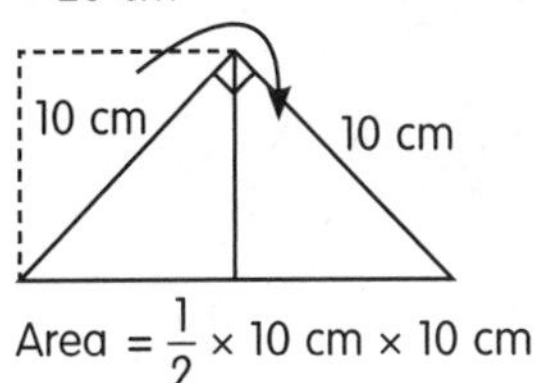

Area $= \frac{1}{2} \times 10 \text{ cm} \times 10 \text{ cm}$
$= 50 \text{ cm}^2$

3. Step 1: Divide each square into quarters.

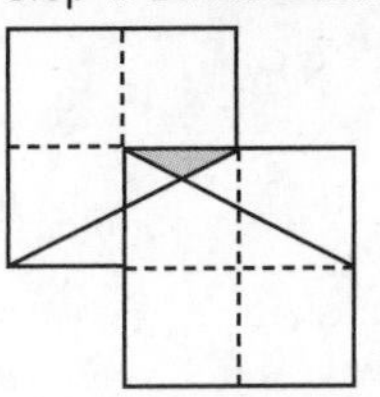

Step 2: Divide each quarter into four rectangles.

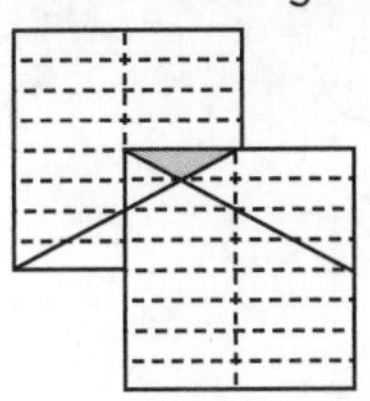

The figure is made up of 28 rectangles. Since the area of the shaded region is half of a rectangle, the fraction of the figure that is shaded is $\frac{1}{2} \times \frac{1}{28} = \frac{1}{56}$.

4. Area of A = Area of B $= \frac{1}{4} \text{ m}^2$
Area of C = Area of E $= \frac{1}{16} \text{ m}^2$
Area of D = Area of F = Area of G
$= \frac{1}{8} \text{ m}^2$

5.

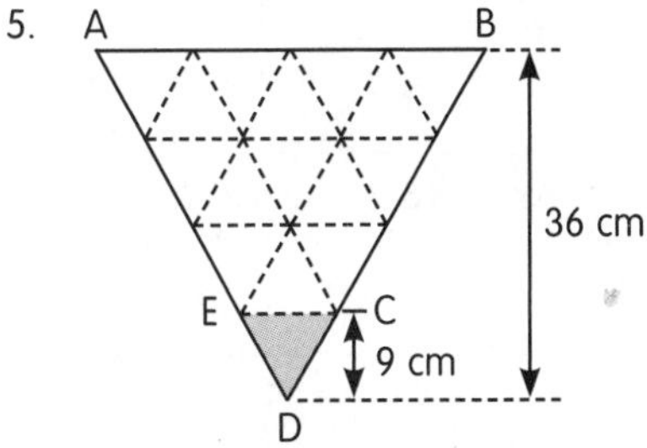

Divide the figure into triangles that are identical to triangle CDE.
Fraction of triangle ABD that is shaded $= \frac{1}{16}$

6. Divide the figure into triangles as shown below.

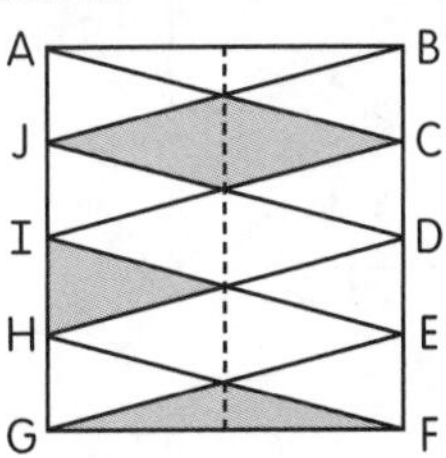

Fraction of figure that is shaded $= \frac{1}{4}$

7. Area of triangle PTV
$= \frac{1}{2} \times (10 \text{ cm} + 6 \text{ cm}) \times 10 \text{ cm}$
$= 80 \text{ cm}^2$

Area of triangle PQR

$= \frac{1}{2} \times 10 \text{ cm} \times (10 \text{ cm} - 6 \text{ cm})$

$= 20 \text{ cm}^2$

Area of triangle RST $= \frac{1}{2} \times 6 \text{ cm} \times 6 \text{ cm}$

$= 18 \text{ cm}^2$

Area of shaded region

$= (10 \text{ cm} \times 10 \text{ cm}) + (6 \text{ cm} \times 6 \text{ cm}) - 80 \text{ cm}^2 - 20 \text{ cm}^2 - 18 \text{ cm}^2$

$= 18 \text{ cm}^2$

8.

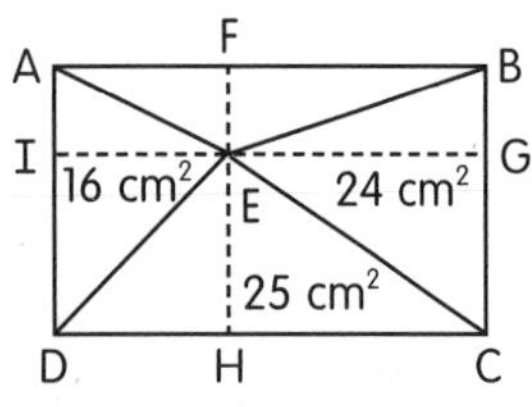

Since AD = BC and IE = DH,

Area of triangle AED $= \frac{1}{2} \times \text{AD} \times \text{IE}$

$= \frac{1}{2} \times \text{AD} \times \text{DH}$

$= 16 \text{ cm}^2$

Area of rectangle AFHD $= \text{AD} \times \text{DH}$

$= 2 \times 16 \text{ cm}^2$

$= 32 \text{ cm}^2$

Since EG = HC,

Area of triangle EBC $= \frac{1}{2} \times \text{BC} \times \text{EG}$

$= \frac{1}{2} \times \text{BC} \times \text{HC}$

$= 24 \text{ cm}^2$

Area of rectangle FBCH $= \text{BC} \times \text{HC}$

$= 2 \times 24 \text{ cm}^2$

$= 48 \text{ cm}^2$

Area of rectangle ABCD $= 32 \text{ cm}^2 + 48 \text{ cm}^2$

$= 80 \text{ cm}^2$

Area of triangle AEB

$= 80 \text{ cm}^2 - 16 \text{ cm}^2 - 25 \text{ cm}^2 - 24 \text{ cm}^2$

$= 15 \text{ cm}^2$

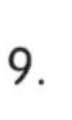

9.

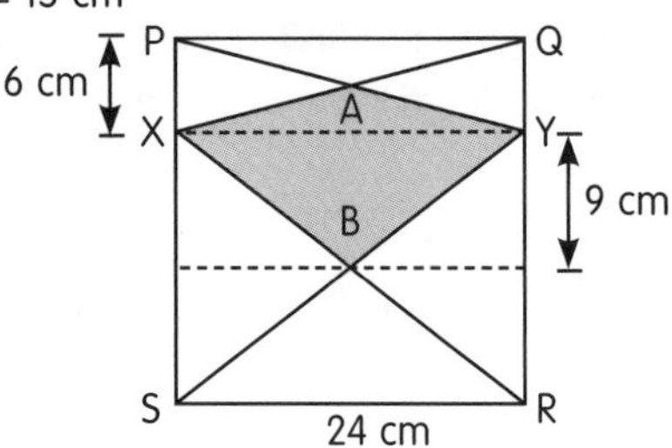

$\text{PX} = \frac{1}{4} \text{PS} = \frac{1}{4} \times 24$

$= 6 \text{ cm}$

$\text{XS} = 18 \text{ cm}$

Height of triangle B $= 18 \text{ cm} \div 2$

$= 9 \text{ cm}$

Area of triangle A $= \frac{1}{2} \times \text{XY} \times \frac{1}{2} \text{PX}$

$= \frac{1}{2} \times 24 \text{ cm} \times 3 \text{ cm}$

$= 36 \text{ cm}^2$

Area of triangle B $= \frac{1}{2} \times \text{XY} \times 9 \text{ cm}$

$= \frac{1}{2} \times 24 \text{ cm} \times 9 \text{ cm}$

$= 108 \text{ cm}^2$

Area of shaded region $= 36 \text{ cm}^2 + 108 \text{ cm}^2$

$= 144 \text{ cm}^2$

10.

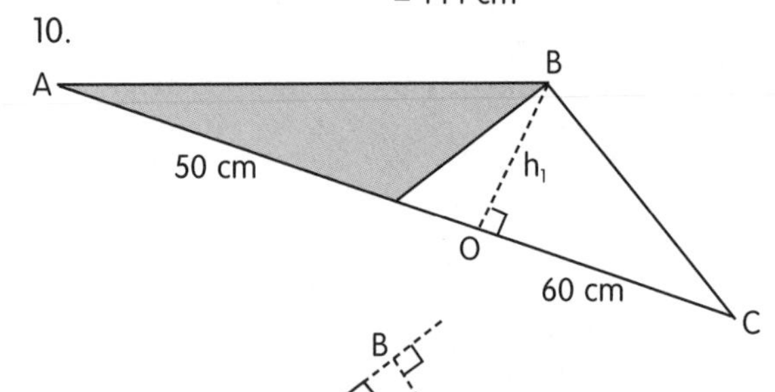

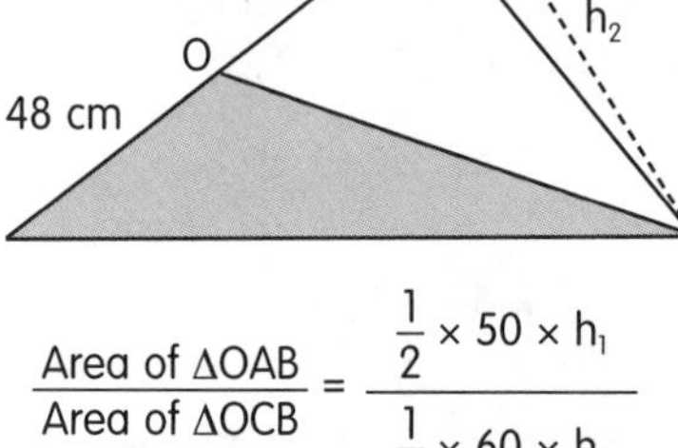

$$\frac{\text{Area of } \Delta\text{OAB}}{\text{Area of } \Delta\text{OCB}} = \frac{\frac{1}{2} \times 50 \times h_1}{\frac{1}{2} \times 60 \times h_1} = \frac{5}{6}$$

$$\frac{\text{Area of } \Delta\text{OCD}}{\text{Area of } \Delta\text{OCB}} = \frac{\frac{1}{2} \times 48 \times h_2}{\frac{1}{2} \times 40 \times h_2} = \frac{6}{5}$$

$$\frac{\text{Area of } \Delta\text{OAB}}{\text{Area of } \Delta\text{OCD}}$$

$$= \frac{\text{Area of } \Delta\text{OAB}}{\text{Area of } \Delta\text{OCB}} \times \frac{\text{Area of } \Delta\text{OCB}}{\text{Area of } \Delta\text{OCD}}$$

$$= \frac{5}{6} \times \frac{5}{6}$$

$$= \frac{25}{36}$$

11.

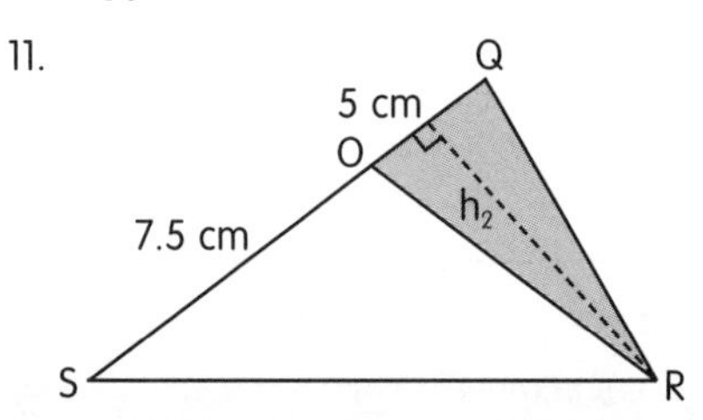

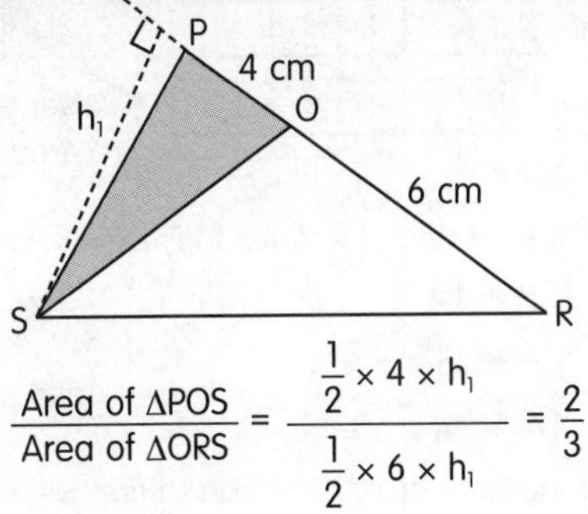

$$\frac{\text{Area of } \Delta POS}{\text{Area of } \Delta ORS} = \frac{\frac{1}{2} \times 4 \times h_1}{\frac{1}{2} \times 6 \times h_1} = \frac{2}{3}$$

$$\frac{\text{Area of } \Delta QOR}{\text{Area of } \Delta ORS} = \frac{\frac{1}{2} \times 5 \times h_2}{\frac{1}{2} \times 7.5 \times h_2} = \frac{2}{3}$$

$$\frac{\text{Area of } \Delta POS}{\text{Area of } \Delta QOR}$$

$$= \frac{\text{Area of } \Delta POS}{\text{Area of } \Delta ORS} \times \frac{\text{Area of } \Delta ORS}{\text{Area of } \Delta QOR}$$

$$= \frac{2}{3} \times \frac{3}{2}$$

$$= \frac{1}{1}$$

5 Ratio

Practice Questions (pp. 60–64)

1. 20 marbles
2. 33 people
3. 10 more boys
4. 1 : 3
5. 7 : 19
6. 88 coins
7. Oranges | 18 kg
   Pineapples

   3 units → 18 kg
   1 unit → 18 kg ÷ 3 = 6 kg
   11 units → 11 × 6 kg = 66 kg
   Total weight of oranges and pineapples
   = 66 kg

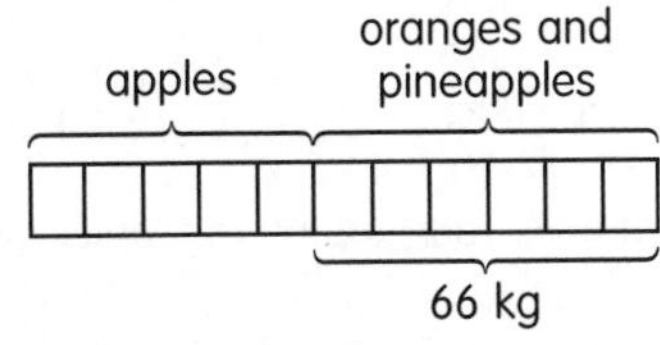

   6 units → 66 kg
   1 unit → 66 kg ÷ 6 = 11 kg
   11 units → 11 × 11 kg = 121 kg
   Total weight of the fruits = 121 kg
8. Tim's current age
   = 25 years + 10 years
   = 35 years

	Jay	:	Tim	:	Angela
	3	:	7	:	9
Current age	15	:	35	:	45
5 years' time	20	:	40	:	50
	2	:	4	:	5

9. After
   Since Joyce and Leslie spent the same amount of money, the difference in their amount of money left remains the same.

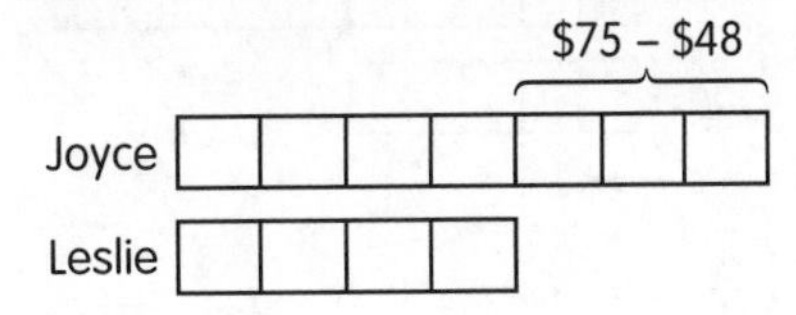

   3 units → $75 – $48 = $27
   1 unit → $27 ÷ 3 = $9
   7 units → 7 × $9 = $63
   4 units → 4 × $9 = $36
   Amount of money Joyce had left = $63
   Amount of money Leslie had left = $36
10. Before

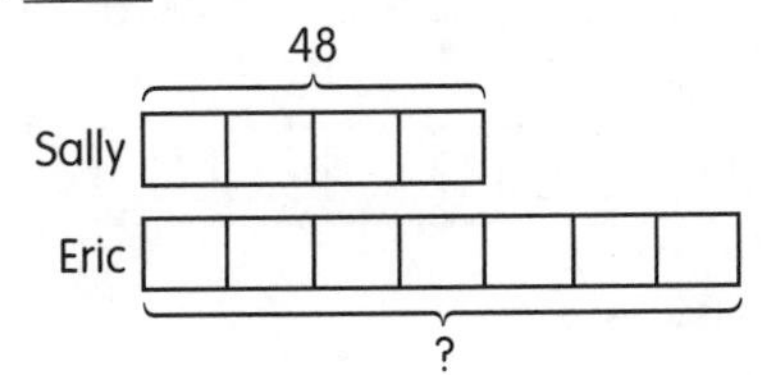

   4 units → 48
   1 unit → 48 ÷ 4 = 12
   7 units → 7 × 12 = 84
   Number of stickers Eric have = 84
   Number of stickers Sally have now
   = 48 + 8
   = 56
   New ratio of the number of Sally's stickers to the number of Eric's stickers
   = 56 : 84 = 2 : 3
11. After

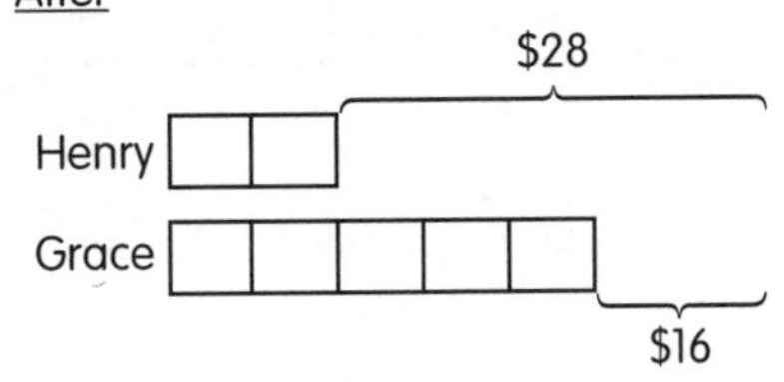

   3 units → $28 – $16 = $12
   1 unit → $12 ÷ 3 = $4
   2 units → 2 × $4 = $8
   Amount of money Henry had
   = $8 + $28
   = $36
   Amount of money Grace had
   = (5 × $4) + $16
   = $36

Challenging Problems (pp. 67–71)

1. $16
2. Before

Michael 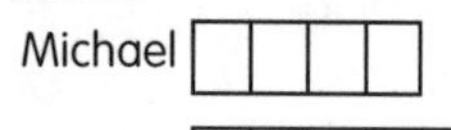

Janet

After

Janet

6 units → 24
1 unit → $24 \div 6 = 4$
4 units → $4 \times 4 = 16$
Number of books Michael had at first = 16

3. Before

Adrian

Susan

After

Adrian

Susan

21

7 units → 21
1 unit → $21 \div 7 = 3$
6 units → $6 \times 3 = 18$
Number of crayons Adrian had at first = 18

4. Before

Elaine

Lynn

After

Elaine

Lynn

$15

3 units → $15
1 unit → $15 ÷ 3 = $5
10 units → 10 × $5 = $50
Amount of money Elaine had at first = $50

5. Boys

Girls

7 units → $216 - 48 = 168$
1 unit → $168 \div 7 = 24$
6 units → $6 \times 24 = 144$
Number of boys who wear glasses = 144

6. Joe

Fred

given to Fred

15

Number of units Joe gave to Fred = 5
5 [ ] → 15
1 [ ] → $15 \div 5 = 3$
16 [ ] → $16 \times 3 = 48$
Number of marbles Joe had at first = 48

7. 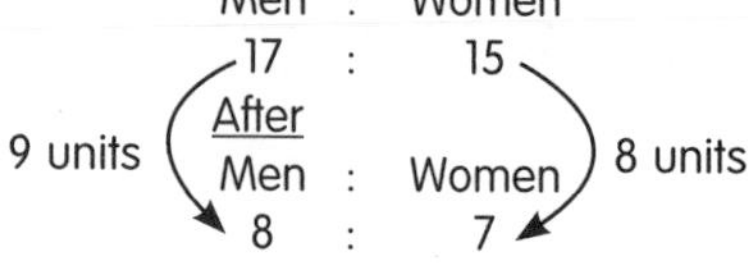

9 units → 90 men
1 unit → 10 men
8 units → 80 women
1 unit → 10 women
Total number of units at first = 17 + 15
= 32
Total number of people who registered
= 32 × 10
= 320

8. Number of Boys : Number of Girls
= 2 : 3
= 14 : 21

Number of Girls : Number of Teachers
= 7 : 4
= 21 : 12

Number of Boys : Number of Girls : Number of Teachers
= 14 : 21 : 12

Number of units representing students
= 14 + 21 = 35
Number of Students : Number of Teachers
= 35 : 12

9. David : Tom
= 4 : 5

Tom : Jack
= 7 : 8

David : Tom : Jack
= 28 : 35 : 40
Number of units Jack has more than David
= 40 – 28
= 12
12 units → 24
1 unit → $24 \div 12 = 2$
35 units → $35 \times 2 = 70$
Number of cards Tom has = 70

10. Weight : Gold coins : Silver coins
= 1 : 5 : 4
= 10 : 50 : 40
= 4 : 20 : 16
= 6 : 30 : 24
10 weights can balance either 50 gold coins or 40 silver coins. Since only 20 gold coins are used, the weight of 30 gold coins is to be used by the silver coins.
Total number of silver coins required = 24

6 Decimals

Practice Questions (pp. 75–79)

1. (a) 48,500 (b) 0.0000324
   (c) 157.14
2. 0.75 l
3. \$1.55
4. \$10.76
5. 15 days
6. $\frac{1}{3}$ kg
7. \$285.70
8. 1.52 m – 1.23 m = 0.29 m
   Alex is 0.29 m taller than Cathy.
   Denise's height = 1.23 m – 0.29 m
   = 0.94 m
9. 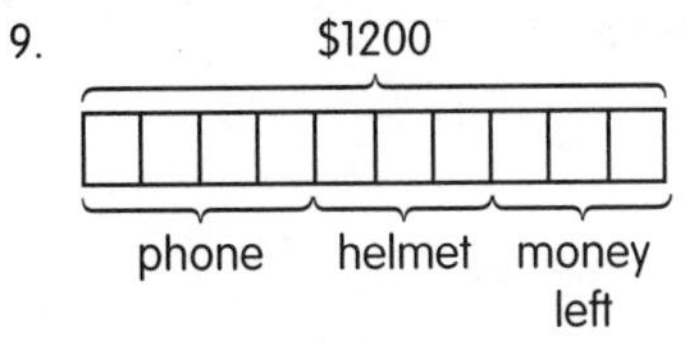

   10 – 4 = 6 units
   0.5 × 6 = 3 units
   10 units ⟶ \$1200
   1 unit ⟶ \$1200 ÷ 10 = \$120
   3 units ⟶ 3 × \$120 = \$360
   Amount of money Roger had left = \$360
10. Amount of money Laurel earned more than Harry = \$0.60 × 5
   = \$3

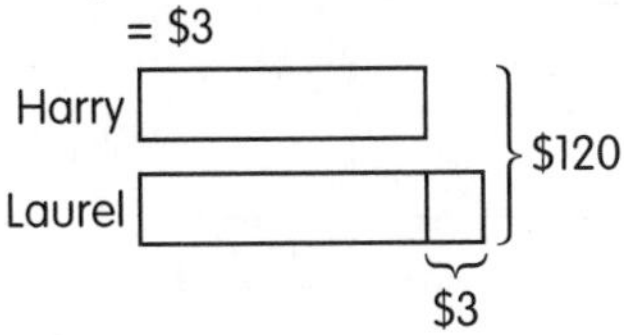

   2 units ⟶ \$120 – \$3 = \$117
   1 unit ⟶ \$117 ÷ 2 = \$58.50
   Amount of money Laurel earned per hour
   = (\$58.50 ÷ 5) + \$0.60
   = \$12.30
11. 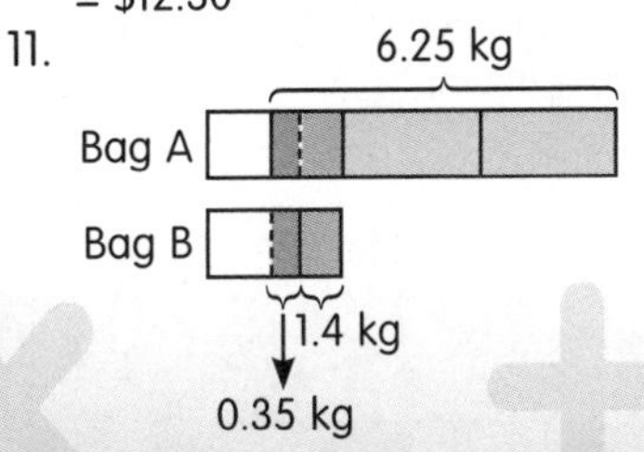

   2 units ⟶ 6.25 kg – 1.4 kg – 0.35 kg
   = 4.5 kg
   1 unit ⟶ 4.5 kg ÷ 2 = 2.25 kg
   New weight of sand in Bag B
   = 2.25 kg – 1.4 kg
   = 0.85 kg

Challenging Problems (pp. 82–86)

1. 3.7
2. Notice that the pattern of 6 digits, 053412, repeats itself in the same order.
   50 = 6 × 8 + 2
   Since 50 is 2 more than 48, which is a multiple of 6, the 50th digit will be the digit 2 places to the right of 1. The 50th digit is 5.
3. $\frac{3}{7}$ = 0.428571 428571...
   21 = 3 × 6 + 3
   Since 21 is 3 more than 18, which is a multiple of 6, the 21st digit will be the digit 3 places to the right of 1. The 21st digit is 8.
4. \$1 + \$0.50 + \$0.20 + \$0.10 + \$0.05 = \$1.85
   Number of coins for each denomination
   = \$42.55 ÷ \$1.85
   = 23
   Total number of coins = 23 × 5
   = 115
5. A slice of cake
   A pie

   15 pies ⟶ 15 × 2 = 30 units
   7 slices of cake ⟶ 7 × 5 = 35 units
   30 + 35 = 65 units ⟶ \$55.25
   1 unit ⟶ \$55.25 ÷ 65 = \$0.85
   Cost of 1 pie = 2 × \$0.85 = \$1.70
   Cost of 2 slices of cake = 10 × \$0.85
   = \$8.50
   Total cost of 1 pie and 2 slices of cake
   = \$1.70 + \$8.50
   = \$10.20
6. R T S T
   69.95 kg 63.10 kg

   Total weight of Robbie, Sarah, and two trophies = 69.95 kg + 63.10 kg
   = 133.05 kg
   (a) Weight of one trophy
   = (133.05 kg – 116.05 kg) ÷ 2
   = 8.5 kg
   (b) Robbie's weight = 69.95 kg – 8.5 kg
   = 61.45 kg
   (c) Sarah's weight = 63.10 kg – 8.5 kg
   = 54.6 kg

7.

Tank A | | 0.45 |

Tank B | | 0.45 | | 0.45 | | 0.45 | | 0.45 | | 0.45 |

2 units ⟶ 12.75 l – (0.45 l × 5) = 10.5 l
1 unit ⟶ 10.5 l ÷ 2 = 5.25 l
3 units ⟶ 3 × 5.25 l = 15.75 l
Initial volume of water in tank B = 15.75 l

8.

Day 1 | |
Day 2 | | $1.40 |
Day 3 | | $1.40 | $1.40 |
Day 4 | | $1.40 | $1.40 | $1.40 |
Day 5 | | $1.40 | $1.40 | $1.40 | $1.40 |
Day 6 | | $1.40 | $1.40 | $1.40 | $1.40 | $1.40 |
Day 7 | | $1.40 | $1.40 | $1.40 | $1.40 | $1.40 | $1.40 |

7 units ⟶ $36.40 – (21 × $1.40) = $7
1 unit ⟶ $7 ÷ 7 = $1
Savings on third day = $1 + $1.40 + $1.40
= $3.80

9.

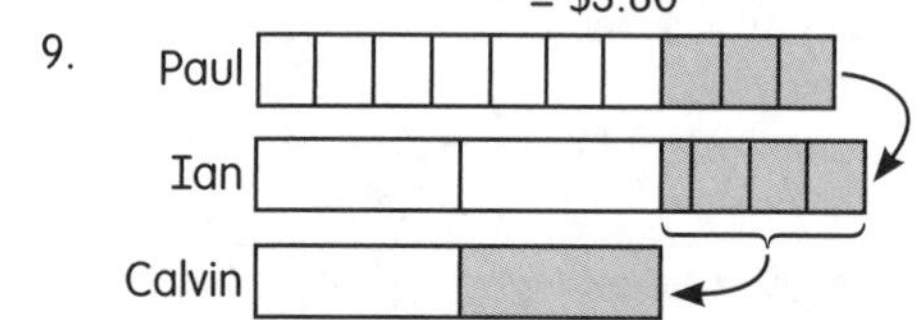

$\frac{2}{3}$ of Ian's money ⟶ 7 units
$\frac{3}{3}$ of Ian's money ⟶ $\frac{7}{2} \times 3 = \frac{21}{2}$ units
$\frac{21}{2} + 7 = \frac{35}{2}$ units ⟶ $63
1 unit ⟶ $63 × $\frac{2}{35}$ = $3.60
10 units ⟶ 10 × $3.60 = $36
Amount of money Paul had at first = $36

10. Amount of money the company would receive if all the plates were not broken
= 78 × $1.50
= $117
Amount of money that the company lost
= $117 – $73
= $44
Amount of money the shop owner would save on each broken plate = $1.50 + $9.50
= $11
Number of broken plates = $44 ÷ $11
= 4

11. $0.45 = \frac{45}{100} = \frac{9}{20}$
$N \times \frac{9}{20}$ = a whole number
We look for a whole number, which is a multiple of 20, between 35 and 45.
The only number N can be is 40.

7 Volume

Practice Questions (pp. 89–94)

1. $\frac{3}{4}$ m
2. 2048 cm^3
3. 1504.8 m^3
4. 3 l 456 ml
5. 8 l 208 ml
6. The block has 8 corners.
Volume of 8 cubes
= 8 × (4 cm × 4 cm × 4 cm)
= 512 cm^3
Volume of remaining block
= (48 cm × 36 cm × 28 cm) – 512 cm^3
= 47,872 cm^3
7. Volume of water in the tank
= 60 cm × 55 cm × 35 cm
= 115,500 cm^3
29.7 l = 29,700 ml = 29,700 cm^3
Volume of water left in the tank
= 115,500 cm^3 – 29,700 cm^3
= 85,800 cm^3
Height of water level in the end = $\frac{85,800}{60 \times 55}$
= 26 cm
8. Increase in volume of water
= 210 l – 140 l
= 70 l
70 l = 70,000 cm^3
1 m = 100 cm
Increase in water level = $\frac{70,000}{100 \times 80}$
= 8.75 cm
9. (a) Volume of box = 8 cm × 8 cm × 1 cm
= 64 cm^3
(b) Volume of box = 6 cm × 6 cm × 2 cm
= 72 cm^3
(c) Volume of box = 4 cm × 4 cm × 3 cm
= 48 cm^3
10.

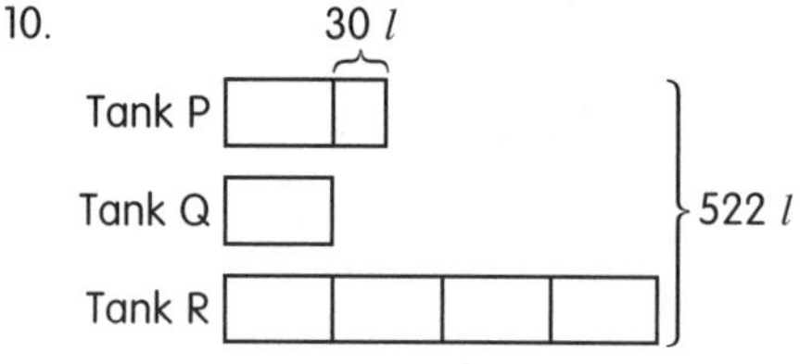

6 units ⟶ 522 l – 30 l = 492 l
1 unit ⟶ 492 l ÷ 6 = 82 l
Capacity of Tank P = 82 l + 30 l
= 112 l
11. Volume of water
= (20 cm × 9 cm × 8 cm) + [(20 – 12) cm × 9 cm × (10 – 8) cm]
= 1584 cm^3

Challenging Problems (pp. 97–101)

1. Original height of water level $= \frac{2}{3} \times 12$ cm
$= 8$ cm
Increase in the height of water level
$= \frac{240 \text{ cm}^3}{20 \text{ cm} \times 16 \text{ cm}}$
$= 0.75$ cm
New height of water level
$= 8$ cm $+ 0.75$ cm
$= 8.75$ cm

2.

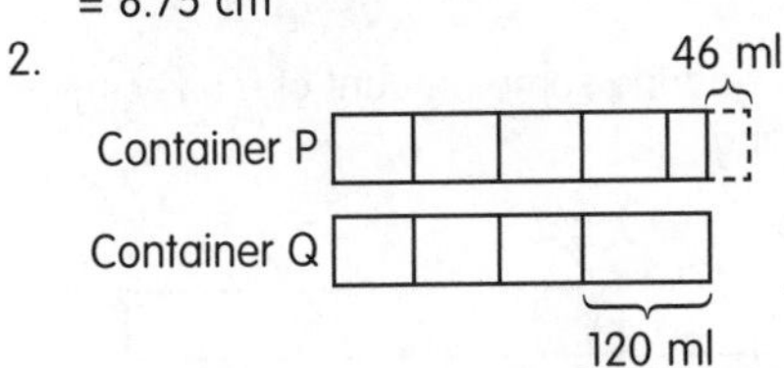

2 units ⟶ 46 ml + 120 ml = 166 ml
1 unit ⟶ 166 ml ÷ 2 = 83 ml
5 units ⟶ 5 × 83 ml = 415 ml
Volume of water in Container P at first
= 415 ml

3. $\frac{2}{3}$ of the tank ⟶ 50 l
$\frac{1}{3}$ of the tank ⟶ 50 l ÷ 2 = 25 l
25 l = 25,000 cm^3
Height of water level at first
$= \frac{25{,}000 \text{ cm}^3}{80 \text{ cm} \times 25 \text{ cm}}$
$= 12.5$ cm

4. Fraction of the tank filled with 30 l of water
$= \frac{4}{5} - \frac{2}{3}$
$= \frac{2}{15}$
$\frac{2}{15}$ of the tank ⟶ 30 l
$\frac{1}{15}$ of the tank ⟶ 30 l ÷ 2 = 15 l
$\frac{4}{5} = \frac{12}{15}$
$\frac{12}{15}$ of the tank ⟶ 12 × 15 l = 180 l
180 l = 180,000 cm^3
Height of the water level at first
$= \frac{180{,}000 \text{ cm}^3}{90 \text{ cm} \times 25 \text{ cm}}$
$= 80$ cm

5. Fraction of tank filled by 6 pails of water
$= \frac{4}{5} - \frac{1}{2}$
$= \frac{3}{10}$
Volume of water in 6 pails
$= \frac{3}{10} \times (120 \text{ cm} \times 100 \text{ cm} \times 80 \text{ cm})$
$= 288{,}000 \text{ cm}^3$
Capacity of each pail $= 288{,}000 \text{ cm}^3 \div 6$
$= 48{,}000 \text{ cm}^3$
$= 48{,}000$ ml

6. Volume of metal cube = 7 cm × 7 cm × 7 cm
$= 343 \text{ cm}^3$
$343 \text{ cm}^3 = 343$ ml
Amount of additional water that the container could hold
= 5500 ml − 2145 ml − 343 ml
= 3012 ml
= 3 l 12 ml

7. Volume of 12 metal cubes
$= 2000 \text{ cm}^3 + 264 \text{ cm}^3 - 764 \text{ cm}^3$
$= 1500 \text{ cm}^3$
Volume of 1 metal cube $= 1500 \text{ cm}^3 \div 12$
$= 125 \text{ cm}^3$
$125 \text{ cm}^2 = 5 \text{ cm} \times 5 \text{ cm} \times 5 \text{ cm}$
Length of each metal cube = 5 cm

8. Capacity of 1 glass = Capacity of 2 cups
Capacity of 4 glasses = Capacity of 8 cups
Capacity of 4 glasses and 7 cups
= Capacity of 15 cups
$\frac{3}{5}$ of the water ⟶ 15 cups
$\frac{1}{5}$ of the water ⟶ 15 ÷ 3 = 5 cups
$\frac{2}{5}$ of the water ⟶ 2 × 5 = 10 cups
Number of cups she could fill = 10

9. Capacity of container

12 bottles   6 bottles + 5 glasses

5 units ⟶ 12 bottles
$2\frac{1}{2}$ units ⟶ 12 ÷ 2 = 6 bottles
$\frac{1}{2}$ unit ⟶ 5 glasses
1 unit ⟶ 2 × 5 = 10 glasses
8 units ⟶ 8 × 10 = 80 glasses
Number of glasses = 80

10. Note that 14 is a multiple of 7 and 15 is a multiple of 5, but 16 is not a multiple of 3. The nearest multiple of 3 from 16 is 15.
Maximum number of blocks
$= \frac{14 \times 15 \times 15}{7 \times 5 \times 3}$
$= 30$

8 Percentage

Practice Questions (pp. 105–108)

1. 36 students
2. 6 votes
3. 20%
4. $170

5. Mint chocolates ☐
Dark chocolates ☐☐☐☐ } 100%

5 units ⟶ 100%
1 unit ⟶ 100% ÷ 5 = 20%
Percentage of mint chocolates = 20%

6. Number of whole numbers from 4 to 23: 20
Numbers in multiples of 5 from 4 to 23:
5, 10, 15, and 20
Percentage = $\frac{4}{20} \times 100\%$
= 20%

7. Number of boys who received prizes
= 20% × 50
= 10
Number of girls who received prizes
= 30% × 30
= 9
Total number of contestants who received prizes = 10 + 9
= 19
Total number of contestants = 50 + 30
= 80
Percentage of contestants who received prizes = $\frac{19}{80} \times 100\%$
= 23.75%

8. Initial price of watch ⟶ 100%
Price after 10% discount ⟶ 90%
Price after increasing the discounted price by 5% = $\frac{105}{100} \times 90\%$
= 94.5%

New percentage discount = $\frac{100\% - 94.5\%}{100\%} \times 100\%$
= 5.5%

9. Derek ☐☐☐☐
Serene ☐☐☐☐☐ } 270

9 units ⟶ 270
1 unit ⟶ 270 ÷ 9 = 30
4 units ⟶ 4 × 30 = 120
Number of stickers Derek has = 120

10. Percentage increase = $\frac{420 - 390}{390} \times 100\%$
= $\frac{30}{390} \times 100\%$
≈ 7.69%

11. Number of male guests = 30% × 120
= 36
Number of male guests who left early
= 25% × 36
= 9
Number of male guests left = 36 − 9
= 27
Total number of guests left = 120 − 9
= 111
New percentage = $\frac{27}{111} \times 100\%$
≈ 24.32%

Challenging Problems (pp. 111–114)

1. A loss of $500.
2. 44%
3. 69%
4. Both had the same amount of money in the end.
5.

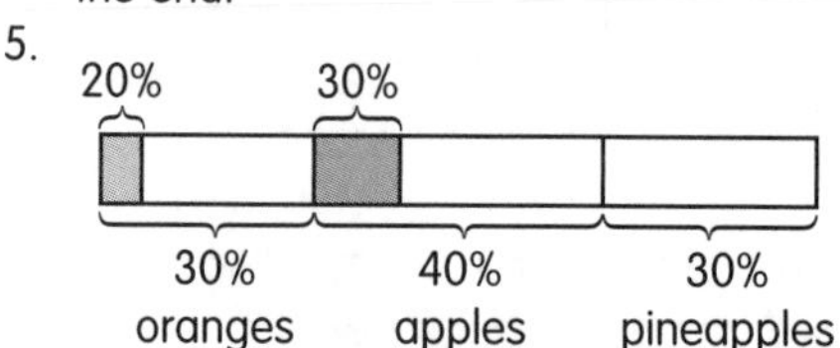

Let the number of fruits be 100.
Number of oranges = 30% × 100
= 30
Number of rotten oranges = 20% × 30
= 6
Number of apples = 40% × 100
= 40
Number of rotten apples = 30% × 40
= 12
Number of fruits that are in good condition = 100 − 18
= 82
Percentage of fruits that are in good condition = $\frac{82}{100} \times 100\%$
= 82%

6.

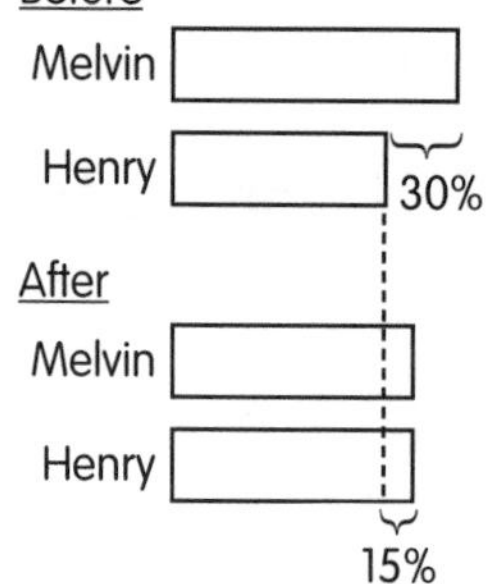

15% of Melvin's marbles ⟶ 30
1% of Melvin's marbles ⟶ 30 ÷ 15 = 2
100% of Melvin's marbles ⟶ 100 × 2 = 200
Number of marbles Henry has = 70% × 200
= 140

7. 60% of Mike's candies ⟶ 24
100% of Mike's candies ⟶ $\frac{24}{60} \times 100 = 40$

Before
Mike 40
Bobby 66

After

Mike | 40 | ? |

Bobby | | |

Difference in the number of candies
= 66 – 40
= 26

Number of candies Bobby must give to Mike = 26 ÷ 2
= 13

8. Number of Singapore coins = 60% × 400
= 240

Number of Malaysia coins = 400 – 240
= 160

New percentage of Malaysia coins
= 40% – 8%
= 32%

32% of coins ⟶ 160
100% of coins ⟶ 500

Number of Singapore coins bought
= 500 – 400
= 100

9. Number of Indonesia stamps = 35% × 400
= 140

Number of Malaysia stamps = 65% × 400
= 260

After 100 stamps were added,
Total number of stamps = 400 + 100
= 500

Number of Malaysia stamps = 70% × 500
= 350

Number of Malaysia stamps added
= 350 – 260
= 90

Number of Indonesia stamps added
= 100 – 90
= 10

10. $\frac{25}{100}$ × Number A = 125

Number A = 125 × $\frac{100}{25}$
= 500

$\frac{0.35}{100}$ × Number B = 10.5

Number B = 10.5 × $\frac{100}{0.35}$
= 3000

Sum = 500 + 3000
= 3500

9 Angles and Triangles

Practice Questions (pp.118–121)

1. ∠x = 86°, ∠y = 52°
2. 118°
3. 35°
4. 21°
5. 54°
6. ∠x = 185°, ∠y = 37°
7. ∠QPR = 52°, ∠PRQ = 52°
8. 60°
9. 22°
10. 134°
11. 68°

Challenging Problems (pp. 123–127)

1. 125°
2. ∠p = 32°, ∠q = 58°
3. ∠PTQ = 180° – 52°
= 128°

∠a = (180° – 128°) ÷ 2
= 26°

∠PTS = 180° – 90° – 26°
= 64°

∠b = 52° + 64°
= 116°

4. ∠PRQ = 180° – 90° – 68°
= 22°

∠TRS = 60°

∠z = 180° – 22° – 60°
= 98°

5. ∠PSX = 180° – 90° – 62°
= 28°

∠XSY = 90° – 28°
= 62°

∠XYS = 180° – 111°
= 69°

∠a = 180° – 62° – 69°
= 49°

6. ∠PQO = 64°

∠YAP = ∠QPO
= 180° – 64° – 52°
= 64°

7. **Method 1**

∠VXW = 180° – 90° – 73°
= 17°

∠YZX = 180° – 90° – 48°
= 42°

∠p = 17° + 42°
= 59°

Method 2

∠VXW = 180° – 90° – 73°
= 17°

∠YXU = 90° – 17°
= 73°

∠p = 180° – 48° – 73°
= 59°

8. ∠QRS = 60°

∠QRP = (180° – 28°) ÷ 2
= 76°

∠y = 76° – 60°
= 16°

9. ∠TPQ = 180° – 90° – 17°
= 73°

∠TPR = 73° – 32°
= 41°

$\angle STP = \angle SPT = 41°$
$\angle y = 180° - (2 \times 41°)$
$= 98°$

10. Since the sum of the angles in a triangle is 180°,
$\angle a + \angle c + \angle e = 180°$
$\angle b + \angle d + \angle f = 180°$
$\angle a + \angle b + \angle c + \angle d + \angle e + \angle f$
$= 180° + 180°$
$= 360°$

10 Quadrilaterals

Practice Questions (pp. 131–134)

1. 25°
2. 75°
3. 51°
4. 40°
5. $\angle BCD = 74°$, $\angle ABC = 106°$, $\angle DAB = 74°$
6. $\angle ABC = 112°$, $\angle BCD = 68°$, $\angle CDA = 112°$
7. 52°
8. 42°
9. $\angle RQS = (180° - 62°) \div 2$
$= 59°$
$\angle PQS = 180° - 59°$
$= 121°$
$\angle x = 121°$
$\angle y = 180° - 121°$
$= 59°$
10. $\angle BED = 180° - 130°$
$= 50°$
$\angle EAD = \angle EDA = 50° \div 2$
$= 25°$
$\angle ADC = 25° + 130°$
$= 155°$

Challenging Problems (pp. 136–140)

1. $\angle IHF = 180° - 89°$
$= 91°$
$\angle GHF = 180° - 91°$
$= 89°$
$\angle FGH = 180° - 89° \div 2$
$= 45.5°$
2. $\angle LPM = \angle LMP$
$= (180° - 90°) \div 2$
$= 45°$
$\angle KPN = 180° - 90° - 28°$
$= 62°$
$\angle NPM = 180° - 62° - 45°$
$= 73°$
3. $\angle PRS = 180° - 42° - 74°$
$= 64°$
$\angle RPQ = 180° - 42° - 74°$
$= 64°$
$\angle QRP = 180° - 64° - 64°$
$= 52°$
$\angle SRQ = 52° + 64°$
$= 116°$
4. $\angle ABE = 180° - 90° - 42°$
$= 48°$
$\angle DBC = 180° - 90° - 58°$
$= 32°$
$\angle EBD = 90° - 48° - 32°$
$= 10°$
5. $\angle SRQ = 180° - 56° - 62°$
$= 62°$
$\angle RQS = 56°$
$\angle PQS = 180° - 56° - 62°$
$= 62°$
6. $\angle ABS = \angle SAB$
$= (180° - 90°) \div 2$
$= 45°$
$\angle RBC = 60°$
$\angle ABC = 180° - 45° - 60°$
$= 75°$
7. $\angle PSQ = \angle PQS = 40°$
$\angle QPS = 180° - (2 \times 40°)$
$= 100°$
$\angle RST = 180° - 100° - 40°$
$= 40°$
$\angle QTR = 40° + 42°$
$= 82°$
8. $\angle BQR = 180° - 105°$
$= 75°$
$\angle DCB = 90°$
$\angle BCQ = 180° - 90° - 38°$
$= 52°$
$\angle CBQ = 180° - 52° - 75°$
$= 53°$
9. $\angle CBE = 180° - 63° - 63°$
$= 54°$
$\angle BCD = 180° - 63°$
$= 117°$
$\angle BAE = 117° - 90°$
$= 27°$
$\angle ABC = 180° - 117°$
$= 63°$
$\angle BEA = 180° - 27° - 63° - 54°$
$= 36°$
10. $\angle ABE = \angle DCE = 60° + 90°$
$= 150°$
$\angle BEA = \angle EAB = (180° - 150°) \div 2$
$= 15°$
$\angle CDE = \angle DEC = (180° - 150°) \div 2$
$= 15°$
$\angle x = 60° - 15° - 15°$
$= 30°$

11 Average

Practice Questions (pp. 143–146)

1. The six 3-digit numbers are: 237, 273, 327, 372, 723, and 732

Sum of numbers
= 237 + 273 + 327 + 372 + 723 + 732
= 2664
Average = 2664 ÷ 6
= 444

2. 19 points
3. 71 points
4. 11
5. 80 points
6. 78 points
7. (a) 1950 g (b) 646 g
8. 93 points
9. 85 kg
10. Total number of pages read on first three days = 61 + 49 + 52
= 162
Average = 162 ÷ 3
= 54
Number of pages read on the fourth day
= 54 + 6
= 60

Challenging Problems (pp. 149–152)

1. Total points scored for 6 tests = 6 × 90
= 540
If she had scored 100 points for 5 tests, her lowest score would be = 540 – (5 × 100)
= 40
2. 500.5
3. Total number of customers at first
= 12 × 800
= 9600
New average = $\frac{9600}{12 - 4}$
= 1200
4. Esther
Felicia
George
8 cm
19 cm
3 × 151 cm = 453 cm
3 units ⟶ 453 cm – 8 cm – 19 cm = 426 cm
1 unit ⟶ 426 cm ÷ 3 = 142 cm
Esther's height = 142 cm
Felicia's height = 142 cm + 8 cm
= 150 cm
George's height = 142 cm + 19 cm
= 161 cm
5. Total weight of 5 packages = 5 × 16 kg
= 80 kg
Possible weight of the heaviest package
= 80 kg – 1 kg – 2 kg – 3 kg – 4 kg
= 70 kg
6. Total weight = 9 × 72 kg
= 648 kg
Total weight of the men = 4 × 82 kg
= 328 kg
Total weight of the women
= 648 kg – 328 kg
= 320 kg
Average weight of the women = 320 kg ÷ 5
= 64 kg
7. Since there are 16 terms, the average number is between the 8th and 9th terms. The 8th consecutive odd number is one less than 122, which is 121. Then we count backwards to find the smallest odd number.

9th	Average	8th	7th	6th	5th	4th	3rd	2nd	1st
123	122	121	119	117	115	113	111	109	107

8. Since there are 10 terms, the average number is between the 5th and 6th terms. The 6th consecutive odd number is one more than 100, which is 101. Then we count forward to find the greatest odd number.

1st	2nd	3rd	4th	5th	Average	6th	7th	8th	9th	10th
91	93	95	97	99	100	101	103	105	107	109

Sum = 91 + 109
= 200
9. Total test score of Aaron and Bob = 32
Total test score of Bob and Chris = 36
Total test score of Chris and Dawn = 42
A + B + B + C + C + D = 32 + 36 + 42
$A + \underbrace{B + C}_{36} + \underbrace{B + C}_{36} + D = 110$
A + D = 110 – 36 – 36
= 38
Average test score of Aaron and Dawn
= 38 ÷ 2
= 19
10. To change the average score from 76 to 79, a total of 100 – 79 = 21 points are needed.
Difference in average score = 79 – 76
= 3
Number of tests before the final test
= 21 ÷ 3
= 7
Total number of tests in the year = 7 + 1
= 8

12 Rate

Practice Questions (pp. 155–158)

1. $7.20
2. 5 minutes
3. (a) 480 booklets (b) 25 minutes
4. $37.50
5. Sophie
6. 6360 loaves of bread
7. $850
8. 7.5s

9. **Method 1**

Number of workers	Number of holes	Number of days
10	20	40
20	20	40 ÷ 2 = 20
20	10	20 ÷ 2 = **10**

Method 2

Number of workers	Number of holes	Number of days
10	20	40
10	10	40 ÷ 2 = 20
20	10	20 ÷ 2 = **10**

10. **Method 1**

Number of clerks	Number of documents	Number of days
3	6	12
1	6	12 × 3 = 36
2	6	36 ÷ 2 = 18
2	3	18 ÷ 2 = **9**

Method 2

Number of clerks	Number of documents	Number of days
3	6	12
3	3	12 ÷ 2 = 6
1	3	6 × 3 = 18
2	3	18 ÷ 2 = **9**

Challenging Problems (pp. 160–163)

1. In every hour, Clock B gains an additional 3 min. 3 min is gained in 1 h.
   60 min is gained in $\frac{1}{3} \times 60 = 20$ h
   Number of hours = 20 h
2. In 1 min, cold water flowing from Tap A can fill $\frac{1}{6}$ of the tub.
   In 1 min, hot water flowing from Tap B can fill $\frac{1}{8}$ of the tub.
   In 1 min, water flowing from both taps can fill ⟶ $\frac{1}{6} + \frac{1}{8} = \frac{7}{24}$ of the tub
   Time taken to fill the tub with water
   ⟶ $1 \div \frac{7}{24} = 3\frac{3}{7}$ min
3. Cost for 5 guests to stay at the hotel for 7 days = $2275
   Cost for 3 guests to stay at the hotel for 7 days = ($2275 ÷ 5) × 3 = $1365
   Cost for 3 guests to stay at the hotel for 4 days = ($1365 ÷ 7) × 4 = $780
4. Fare for the first two km = $2.80
   Fare for the next 17.8 km
   = 60 × $0.30
   = $18
   Total fare = $2.80 + $18
   = $20.80
5. (a) Total number of students = 80 + 16
   = 96
   Number of days = $\frac{12 \times 80}{96}$
   = 10
   (b) Total weight of rice = 120 kg + 40 kg
   = 160 kg
   Number of days = $\frac{12 \times 160}{120}$
   = 16
   Additional number of days = 16 − 12
   = 4
6. **Method 1**

Number of men	Number of fences	Number of days
3	5	2
3	1	$\frac{2}{5}$
1	1	$\frac{2}{5} \times 3 = \frac{6}{5}$
2	1	$\frac{6}{5} \div 2 = \mathbf{\frac{3}{5}}$

Method 2

Number of men	Number of fences	Number of days
3	5	2
1	5	2 × 3 = 6
2	5	6 ÷ 2 = 3
2	1	$3 \times \frac{1}{5} = \mathbf{\frac{3}{5}}$

7. **Method 1**

Number of men	Number of days	Number of boxes
6	4	900
10	4	$\frac{900 \times 10}{6} = 1500$
10	6	$\frac{1500 \times 6}{4} = \mathbf{2250}$

Method 2

Number of men	Number of days	Number of boxes
6	4	900
6	6	$\frac{900 \times 6}{4} = 1350$
10	6	$\frac{1350 \times 10}{6} = \mathbf{2250}$

8.

Number of days Aileen takes	Number of days Eve takes	Number of dresses
2	3	48
4	2	64
4	6	48 × 2 = 96

In 4 days, Eve can sew 96 – 64
= 32 dresses.
In 1 day, Eve can sew 32 ÷ 4 = 8 dresses.
Number of days Eve will take to sew
48 dresses = 48 ÷ 8
= 6
In 2 days, Aileen can sew 48 – (3 × 8)
= 24 dresses.
In 1 day, Aileen can sew 24 ÷ 2
= 12 dresses.
Number of days Aileen will take to sew 48
dresses = 48 ÷ 12
= 4

9.

Number of days Simon takes	Number of days Lisa takes	Number of houses
3	1	$\frac{19}{20}$
4	3	$1\frac{3}{5}$
9	3	$\frac{19}{20} \times 3 = 2\frac{17}{20}$

In 5 days, Simon can paint $2\frac{17}{20} - 1\frac{3}{5} = \frac{5}{4}$ houses.
In 4 days, Simon can paint 1 house.
In 3 days, Lisa can paint $1\frac{3}{5} - 1 = \frac{3}{5}$ of a house.
In 5 days, Lisa can paint 1 house.

10. Since Ben takes 6 days to renovate the room, he will take 1 day to renovate $\frac{1}{6}$ of the room. Since James takes 15 days to renovate the room, he will take 1 day to renovate $\frac{1}{15}$ of the room. Using guess and check,

Number of days Ben takes	Number of days James takes	Total number of days	Number of rooms renovated
1	8	9	$\frac{1}{6} + (\frac{1}{15} \times 8) = \frac{7}{10}$
3	6	9	$(\frac{1}{6} \times 3) + (\frac{1}{15} \times 6) = \frac{9}{10}$
4	5	9	$(\frac{1}{6} \times 4) + (\frac{1}{15} \times 5) = 1$

Number of days Ben will take = 4

13 Data Analysis

Practice Questions (pp. 166–171)

1. (a) 27.5% (b) 6 : 5
   (c) 240,000 fans
2. (a) $400 (b) $640
   (c) $700
3. (a) 25 families (b) 24%
   (c) 69 children
4. (a) 14 envelopes (b) 160 stamps
   (c) 860 stamps
5. (a) 50 oranges (b) 15 bananas
   (c) 200 fruits (d) 32.5%
6. (a) 350 fiction books (b) 50 cook books
   (c) 800 books (d) 25%
7. Sum of 6 numbers = 6 × 12
   = 72
   Greatest possible number
   = 72 – (1 + 2 + 3 + 4 + 5)
   = 57

Challenging Problems (pp. 174–178)

1. (a) $\frac{1}{12}$ (b) 126 students
   (c) 189 students (d) $16\frac{2}{3}$%
2. (a) 30 miles
   (b) car = 30 miles; truck = 25 miles
   (c) 9:00 a.m.
3. (a) Data analysis (b) Algebra
   (c) 156 students (d) Geometry
4. (a) $\frac{5}{16}$ (b) 96 m^2
5. 6
6. Sum of numbers in Group A
   = 8 + 6 + 2 + 5
   = 21
   Sum of numbers in Group B
   = 9 + 3 + 5 + 3 + 4
   = 24
   Sum of numbers in both groups = 21 + 24
   = 45
   Mean = 45 ÷ 9
   = 5
   Sum of numbers in Group A after exchange
   = 4 × 5
   = 20
   Sum of numbers in Group B after exchange
   = 5 × 5
   = 25
   Group A needs 1 less and Group B needs 1 more.
   Group A = 6, Group B = 5 or
   Group A = 5, Group B = 4

14 Mixed Problems

Practice Questions (pp. 180–184)

1. Beth = $5, Ruth = $7
2. 9

3. 13, and 29
4. $115
5.

	Short-sighted	Long-sighted	Total
Number of boys	32	19	51
Number of girls	28	25	53
Total	60	44	104

6. 8 cuts
7. Surface area of one side of the square
   = 5 cm × 5 cm
   = 25 cm^2
   There are 24 squares covering the surface of the solid.
   Surface area of solid = 24 × 25 cm^2
   = 600 cm^2
8. 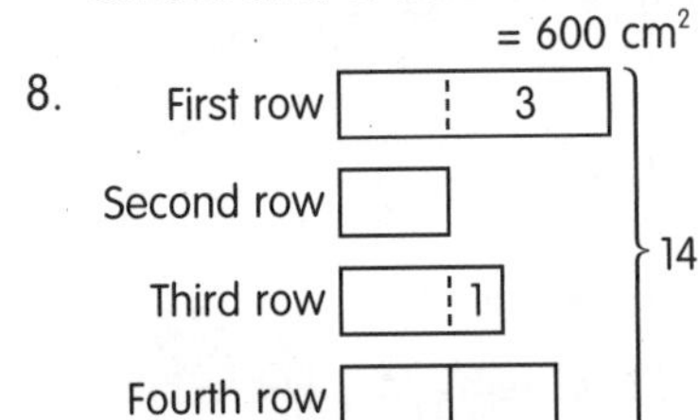

   5 units → 14 – 3 – 1 = 10
   1 unit → 10 ÷ 5 = 2
   Number of coins in first row = 2 + 3
   = 5
   Number of coins in second row = 2
   Number of coins in third row = 2 + 1
   = 3
   Number of coins in fourth row = 2 × 2
   = 4
9. Before
   Henry
   Donald

   After
   Henry
   Donald
   35

   7 units → 35
   1 unit → 35 ÷ 7 = 5
   10 units → 10 × 5 = 50
   Number of pens Donald had at first = 50
10. Area of triangles P and Q = Area of unshaded parts
   Area Q
   Area P
   Area of unshaded parts = 3 units
   Ratio = 1 : 3

Challenging Problems (pp. 186–190)

1. 4, 7, and 9
2. 34,298
3. 2 boys, 5 girls
4. 55¢
5. Number of small rectangles
   = 7 × 9 + 5
   = 68
6. Number of tiles = (14 + 8) × 2
   = 44
7. Timothy
   Paul
   54

   3 units → 54
   1 unit → 54 ÷3 = 18
   2 units → 2 × 18 = 36
   Timothy's age this year = 18 years old
   Paul's age this year = 36 years old
   Difference in age = 18 years
   When Timothy is 36 years old,
   Paul's age → 36 + 18 = 54 years old
   Combined age → 36 + 54 = 90 years old
8. If there were 46 baskets of apples, the number of apples would be 46 × 8 = 368.
   So, the extra 560 – 368 = 192 apples were packed into boxes.
   One basket of apples has 12 more apples than one box of apples.
   So, there are 192 ÷ 12 = 16 boxes of apples.
9. $0.78125 = \frac{78,125}{100,000}$
   $= \frac{125 \times 625}{125 \times 800}$
   $= \frac{625}{800}$
   $= \frac{25 \times 25}{25 \times 32}$
   $= \frac{25}{32}$
10. Number of matches in the first round
   = 32 ÷ 2
   = 16
   Number of matches in the second round
   = 16 ÷ 2
   = 8
   Number of matches in the third round
   = 8 ÷ 2
   = 4
   Number of matches in the fourth round
   = 4 ÷ 2
   = 2
   Number of matches in the fifth round
   = 2 ÷ 2
   = 1
   Total number of matches Terence played
   = 16 + 8 + 4 + 2 + 1
   = 31